LABORATORY MANUAL

FOR

GENERAL CHEMISTRY

DREXEL UNIVERSITY

CHEM 101

CHEM 102

2009-2010 ACADEMIC YEAR

prepared by

Edward J. Thorne

WILEY *Custom*
LEARNING SOLUTIONS

ISBN 978-0-470-58396-8

Printed and bound by Victor Graphics, Inc.

10 9 8 7 6 5 4 3 2 1

TABLE OF CONTENTS

General Course Requirements, Laboratory Reports, and Laboratory Safety   Page 1

Experiment #1 -Stoichiometry and Limiting Reagents . . . . .   Page 8

Experiment #2 - Spectroscopy. . . . .   Page 19

Experiment #3 - Conductivity of Solutions . . . .   Page 29

Experiment #4 - Determination of Molar Mass by Freezing Point Depression   Page 38

Experiment #5 - Preparation of An Ester . . . .   Page 46

Experiment #6 - Kinetics of Alcohol Oxidation . . . .   Page 54

Experiment #7 - Acids and Bases . . . .   Page 67

Experiment #8 - Electrochemical Cells . . . .   Page 78

Experiment #9 - Separating Mixtures by Chromatography . . . .   Page 88

ACKNOWLEDGMENTS

This manual has developed from many years experience with these experiments, and the current version represents the accumulated efforts of many people. The instructors and students who have worked with these experiments in the past have made many worthwhile suggestions.

We are indebted to Dr. Sally Solomon for permission to include the experiment on the Determination of Phosphorus in Plant Food, which has previously been published in her lab manual "Experiments in General Chemistry", published by Wiley Custom Services.

Wolfgang Nadler, head of the Electronics Design and Instrumentation Shop at Drexel's College of Arts and Sciences, designed and built the first detector box for the Gas Chromatography experiment and got it to work. Nick Kwasnjuk, Supervisor of the Machine Shop, and his assistant Zoltan Boldy, made twelve detector boxes. Students Nick Stahl and Massoxi Van Dunem helped to improve the experiment by testing various columns and collecting data on the performance of the gas chromatograph.

Dr. Daniel King provided valuable input in assisting with the modifications necessary to adapt some of the experiments to the LoggerPro data collection system. He also suggested other improvements to several of the remaining experiments.

GENERAL COURSE REQUIREMENTS, LABORATORY REPORTS, AND LABORATORY SAFETY

GENERAL COURSE REQUIREMENTS

This manual has been prepared for the chemistry laboratory segments of CHEM 101 and CHEM 102. It contains all of the laboratory exercises you are required to complete in these courses and has developed from several years' experiences with these experiments. As instructors we have heard all too often the cries of students claiming, "these experiments don't work". Well, they do work very well provided there is sufficient care and preparation toward their completion. Most of the negative comments come from the students who come to the lab asking, "What are we doing today?" Obviously they have not adequately prepared to do anything in the lab on that day, and their unsuccessful experiences result heavily from their inability to "wing it" instead of having a good idea of what was to be done. As we go through life we find it necessary to prepare in some fashion for just about any new activity if we expect it to be successful. You would not set out on a vacation trip by car to some area you are not familiar with unless you have at least looked over some maps and have a general idea of how you are going to proceed. Similarly, you would not set out to prepare a fancy meal without knowing what equipment and supplies are necessary to complete the job. The chemistry lab is no different. If you don't have a general plan of how to proceed when you come to the lab, your chances of success are not very great. You are required to read the experiment before you come to the lab. Don't even think of coming to the lab until you have carefully read the experiment.

This manual treats each experiment separately and summarizes the background principles applicable to each. In general, each experiment in this manual begins with an objective, a statement of just what we are trying to accomplish by doing the experiment. Next is the background, or the theoretical principles involved in each. Keep in mind that the purpose of this lab manual is to correlate these principles to laboratory exercises: it is not supposed to be a textbook of theory. Where appropriate, references will be made to specific pages, figures, or tables of data in your course textbook, Chemistry: The Molecular Science, Third Edition by John W. Moore, Conrad L. Stanitski, and Peter C. Jurs. You should consult your course textbook to find a more detailed discussion of stoichiometry, spectroscopy, kinetics, or whatever the experimental topic happens to be. Next comes

the experimental procedure, which is a step-by-step listing of the operations necessary to accumulate the appropriate data. The data will be recorded on the data page, which you must have signed by your instructor before leaving the lab. One of the primary reasons for having the data sheet signed is to insure that you have collected all of the data necessary to complete the calculations and form your conclusions. You would find it very frustrating if you try to write a lab report and find out that you are missing a few crucial pieces of data. By having your instructor sign your data sheet, he/she will be able to determine whether you have recorded all of the data you will need. A section entitled Treatment of the Data identifies each calculation, graph, or balanced equation that you are required to complete based on your accumulated data. This section will tell precisely what must be included in the Calculations section of your lab report.

You will be required to submit a **legible, handwritten** Procedure section of your lab report **before** doing the experiment. This will demonstrate your level of preparation for the experiment to be done. Late submission of the Procedure will not be accepted so you will forfeit 5 points of the report grade.

If you miss your regularly scheduled lab session, it would be best to try and make it up by attending another section. Of course you will need the permission and data sheet signature of the instructor whose section you want to attend and this generally will be no problem as long as there is available room in the lab at that time. We are not permitted to conduct laboratory classes with more than 24 students in the lab, so you will only be allowed to attend another lab section if there are less than 24 students in that class. There will be a single make-up day for any missed experiments but waiting for this could cause some difficulties because it shifts your workload to the end of the quarter when you will need more time to prepare for final exams. This single make-up day will not be run until all of the experiments have been completed, so it will, of necessity, be near the end of the quarter. Normally, that means the make-up day for missed labs will be held during the tenth week of the quarter.

LABORATORY OPERATION

When you arrive at the lab for your class, all of the necessary equipment, glassware, and/or chemicals will be located on the front bench and/or in the fume hoods. It is set up this way to make it easier to carry out each experiment. By doing this, it is not necessary for you to go to the storeroom,

wait in line, sign out all of the necessary equipment and leave your I.D. card until the supplies are returned. As a courtesy to the other classes that will come after you, you are expected to leave the lab in the same general condition you found it. This means that at the end of each experiment you are required to rinse clean any glassware or equipment you used, all chemicals are to be returned to their respective storage place, and all trash and other refuse is to be disposed of in the appropriate containers. If it becomes apparent that certain lab section classes are unable or unwilling to adhere to this common courtesy practice, it may be necessary to institute a process in which you will have to acquire any necessary supplies from the storeroom. For obvious reasons, this is certainly not the preferred method of conducting a lab class, but it will be instituted if necessary.

LABORATORY REPORTS

Writing a report that describes, explains, and makes conclusions based on your work is just as much a part of your work as the actual experimental manipulations. Great inventions, discoveries, new synthetic techniques, etc. are useless unless they can be accurately and clearly related to the rest of the technical community. Every technical journal in press at the present time has its own format requirements for manuscripts, and authors must adhere to the prescribed format as a requirement for publication. Similarly, there is a format that must be adhered to for reports in this course. While this is not a technical writing course, at this stage of your academic career you are expected to be gaining experience in writing in a clear and concise fashion, following the accepted rules of grammar. The reports will not be graded on a basis of penalizing strictly for grammatical errors, such as punctuation, etc., but points will be deducted for flagrant violations of writing practices. In the past, students have submitted reports with incomplete sentences and other errors that are more a result of carelessness and/or laziness than grammatical errors. Most important of all, proofread your reports before they are submitted. Reports submitted with incomplete sentences and other serious grammatical errors will be penalized heavily, sometimes up to 50% or more of the point value for the section of the report where they are found.

Your lab report is due before the building closes on the day one week after you perform the lab, unless otherwise instructed. Five points will be deducted for each class day the report is late and any report submitted more than two weeks late (that would be three weeks after completing the

experiment) is worth zero points. Since each experiment is different, emphasizing different principles, each report will be different. At the end of each experiment in this manual, the requirements for the lab report pertaining to that experiment are detailed. Your report must adhere to these requirements. In most instances the total point value of the report will be 80%, with the balance being made up by your signed data page(s), which must be included with each lab report.

PLAGIARISM POLICY

The reports you submit must be your own original work and not simply a copy from this lab manual, some other book, and/or other students' reports. The objective is for you to demonstrate YOUR understanding and ability to make conclusions, not information and/or conclusions derived from some other outside source(s). Any clear cases of plagiarism will result in a grade of zero.

All of the experiments in this manual will be completed by working in groups but each student is responsible for writing and submitting his/her own lab report unless you are otherwise instructed. Each person is responsible for individually demonstrating his or her level of understanding of the experiment. This is not to say that you should not consult with each other: quite the opposite. It is good to work together and discuss the calculations and other aspects of the report. When it finally comes down to demonstrating your understanding of the principles and transferring the data to a conclusion, each of you must work individually.

LABORATORY SAFETY

To maintain the laboratory as a safe place to work, you are required to adhere to the safety rules detailed below. Any deviation from these rules will result in verbal warnings and failure to adhere to those warnings could mean expulsion from the lab and will affect your grade.

1. Horseplay or clowning around will not be tolerated at any time.

2. Food and/or drink are **NEVER** permitted in the laboratories because accidental contamination could lead to poisoning.

3. All places where hazardous substances are used will be indicated by special **CAUTION** notices and special instructions. Please pay close attention to these to avoid injury.

4. Spills on your clothing or skin must be treated immediately by rinsing with large amounts of water. Notify your lab instructor if there is some question about possible problems with a spill. There is a water station with a shower and an eyewash fountain in each lab.

5. Safety glasses or goggles must be worn **<u>covering your eyes</u>** (not around your neck or covering your forehead) at all times when you are in the laboratory, even when you are not working. Goggles and/or safety glasses are available in the school store or other outside sources. Be sure you purchase them before you come to your first laboratory period. If you do not have the necessary eye protection, you will not be permitted to work in the lab. The Chemistry storeroom is not responsible for supplying safety glasses for your use. Contact lenses are **<u>NEVER</u>** permitted in the laboratory (even with safety glasses or goggles) as they could make your eye more vulnerable to vapors.

6. Bare legs and open shoes, such as sandals, are prohibited for obvious reasons. Spills can be more dangerous if they make direct contact with bare skin instead of clothing. If you come to the lab and are wearing short pants, you will be required to wear a full-length lab coat to protect your skin. **IMPORTANT!! In case of a spill on your clothing, do not try to save your clothing first. Do not run to the washroom. USE THE SHOWER.**

7. Do not force glass tubing or thermometers through a rubber or cork stopper. The places in each procedure where this may be encountered will be marked with a **CAUTION** notation. Broken or cracked glassware should be discarded immediately. Be sure to dispose of any glass or metal in the waste containers in each lab. **<u>NEVER</u>** put any type of broken or disposable glass (such as Pasteur pipets) into the waste paper containers. Do not put paper in the containers designated for glass and metal waste.

8. There is a fire blanket near every laboratory and a fire extinguisher in each lab. If your clothing catches fire, **DO NOT RUN**. Instead, wrap the fire blanket around you to extinguish the flames.

At your first lab meeting of CHEM 101, you are required to read the following statement carefully, tear it out of your lab manual, sign it, and turn it in to your instructor.

I have read the information on pages 1 through 5 of this manual and I agree to abide by it completely. A few of the most important topics discussed on these pages include the following:

- To properly prepare for any experiment I am required to read it over and formulate a general plan of how to proceed before doing any experiment.

- I am required to submit a **legible, handwritten** Procedure section of my lab report **before** doing the experiment. Late submission of the Procedure will not be accepted so I will forfeit 5 points of the report grade if it is not done on time.

- Laboratory reports are due one week from the day the experiment is completed and five points will be deducted for each day the report is late. The reports I submit must be my own original words.

- There is to be no food or drink brought into the lab at any time.

- Safety glasses or goggles **MUST** be worn at all times when I am in the laboratory, even when I am not working. If I do not bring the necessary eye protection, I will not be permitted to work in the lab. The Chemistry storeroom is not responsible for supplying safety glasses for my use. Contact lenses are **NEVER** permitted in the laboratory (even with safety glasses or goggles).

- No open shoes (sandals) or bare legs (shorts) are permitted in the lab at any time.

- Playing around is not tolerated in the lab at any time.

- All equipment and chemicals are to be returned to their appropriate storage space at the end of the experiment.

PRINT YOUR NAME_____

SIGN HERE_____   DATE_____

At your first lab meeting of CHEM 102, you are required to read the following statement carefully, tear it out of your lab manual, sign it, and turn it in to your instructor.

I have read the information on pages 1 through 5 of this manual and I agree to abide by it completely. A few of the most important topics discussed on these pages include the following:

- To properly prepare for any experiment I am required to read it over and formulate a general plan of how to proceed before doing any experiment.

- I am required to submit a **legible, handwritten** Procedure section of my lab report **before** doing the experiment. Late submission of the Procedure will not be accepted so I will forfeit 5 points of the report grade if it is not done on time.

- Laboratory reports are due one week from the day the experiment is completed and five points will be deducted for each day the report is late. The reports I submit must be my own original words.

- There is to be no food or drink brought into the lab at any time.

- Safety glasses or goggles **MUST** be worn at all times when I am in the laboratory, even when I am not working. If I do not bring the necessary eye protection, I will not be permitted to work in the lab. The Chemistry storeroom is not responsible for supplying safety glasses for my use. Contact lenses are **NEVER** permitted in the laboratory (even with safety glasses or goggles).

- No open shoes (sandals) or bare legs (shorts) are permitted in the lab at any time.

- Playing around is not tolerated in the lab at any time.

- All equipment and chemicals are to be returned to their appropriate storage space at the end of the experiment.

PRINT YOUR NAME_____

SIGN HERE_____ DATE_____

EXPERIMENT #1 - STOICHIOMETRY AND LIMITING REAGENTS

OBJECTIVE

This experiment is designed to demonstrate the principles of stoichiometry as applied to a chemical reaction in solution. By adjusting the relative amounts of the reactants involved, the effect of limiting reagents is illustrated.

BACKGROUND

Stoichiometry is the process of "keeping track" of the amounts of reactants and products involved in a chemical reaction. The calculations are based on the use of a balanced chemical equation, which gives the ratios in which the reactants combine and products form. In this experiment we are going to study the following reaction:

$$CaCl_{2(aq)} + 2\ NaOH_{(aq)} \rightarrow Ca(OH)_{2(s)} + 2\ NaCl_{(aq)}$$

This equation states that two moles of NaOH are needed to react with one mole of $CaCl_2$ to produce one mole of solid $Ca(OH)_2$ and two moles of NaCl. The subscript (aq) indicates that the material is present as an aqueous solution, or dissolved in water.

Very often, the reactants may not be mixed in exactly the right proportions and a limiting reagent condition results. These problems are not unlike many everyday experiences; they only seem to be different because of the units involved for what we are trying to "keep track of" in the problem. As an analogy, consider the following scenario. Let's suppose that you are working in an assembly plant manufacturing cars. Your job is to put the tires on the finished car bodies. You know that every car coming down the assembly line needs four tires to complete your job so, in a sense, you can write the following balanced equation:

$$1\ car\ body + 4\ tires \rightarrow 1\ completed\ car$$

While this is not a chemical equation, it nevertheless is an expression relating your "reactants" (car bodies and tires) to the "products" (the completed car). You report to work and find that there are 50 car bodies and 160 tires: you have a "limiting reagent problem". If you were asked how many cars you could assemble, you could give two different answers but only one of them is correct. Based

on the number of car bodies (forget about the tires for a moment) you would say that you could assemble 50 completed cars. However, based on the number of tires (forget about the car bodies this time) you figure that you can assemble 40 completed cars because you have 160 tires and each car needs four tires, so you can assemble (160/4) completed cars. Clearly the tires are the "limiting reagent" because you don't have enough tires for all of the car bodies that are available. Similarly, the car bodies are the "excess reagent". The net result is that you can make 40 completed cars, and you would have 10 car bodies left "unreacted". Limiting reagent problems in chemistry are very similar except that we don't count car bodies and tires: instead we count moles of atoms or molecules. Let's go back to the balanced equation for the reaction we are studying:

$$CaCl_{2(aq)} + 2\ NaOH_{(aq)} \rightarrow Ca(OH)_{2(s)} + 2\ NaCl_{(aq)}$$

Suppose we start a reaction using 2.0 moles of $CaCl_2$ and 3.0 moles of NaOH. How much $Ca(OH)_2$ will form? To solve the problem, we treat it as two separate problems: one based on the amount of available $CaCl_2$ and the other based on the amount of available NaOH. The conversion factors we need come from the balanced equation, which gives us the reacting ratios. First, for $CaCl_2$:

$$2.0\ mol\ CaCl_2\ \times\ \frac{1\ mol\ Ca(OH)_2}{1\ mol\ CaCl_2} = 2.0\ mol\ Ca(OH)_2$$

Next, we repeat the calculation based on the amount of NaOH (forgetting about the $CaCl_2$ this time) we find:

$$3.0\ mol\ NaOH\ \times\ \frac{1\ mol\ Ca(OH)_2}{2\ mol\ NaOH} = 1.5\ mol\ Ca(OH)_2$$

The correct answer is always the smaller of the two values as obtained above. Therefore, the final result is that we could only form 1.5 moles of $Ca(OH)_2$ and there would be left some unreacted $CaCl_2$. Can you figure how much $CaCl_2$ would be left unreacted? The maximum amount of $Ca(OH)_2$ that we can expect to form, based on the limiting reactant, is called the theoretical yield. In this example, it is 1.5 moles of $Ca(OH)_2$.

In this experiment, you are going to keep the amount of $CaCl_2$ constant and gradually change the amount of NaOH. Initially the $CaCl_2$ will be in excess but at some point it will become the limiting reagent. We are going to construct a graph that will show the maximum amount of $Ca(OH)_2$ that can be formed from the amount of $CaCl_2$ used. For example, let us suppose that you conducted a study between two species (not necessarily those you are using in this experiment) and you obtained the

following data relating the amounts of the reactants (A and B) to the mass of product (C) that was obtained after drying. NOTE: These values are for demonstration purposes only and may not be close to the values you will obtain.

VOLUME OF A (ml)	VOLUME OF B (ml)	MASS OF C OBTAINED (grams)
5.00	2.00	1.25
5.00	3.50	2.15
5.00	5.00	2.15
5.00	7.50	2.15

In this case, component A will become the limiting reagent because adjusting the amounts of B gave different amounts of C, up to some limiting value. We can also add the point (0,0) to the data because if no B has been added, then no product C could have formed. This just makes the graph "more complete" and helps to emphasize the point where the limiting amount has been reached. We then construct a graph showing the volume of B (which becomes the excess reagent) on the x-axis and the mass of C (the final product) on the y-axis. The graph of these data is as follows:

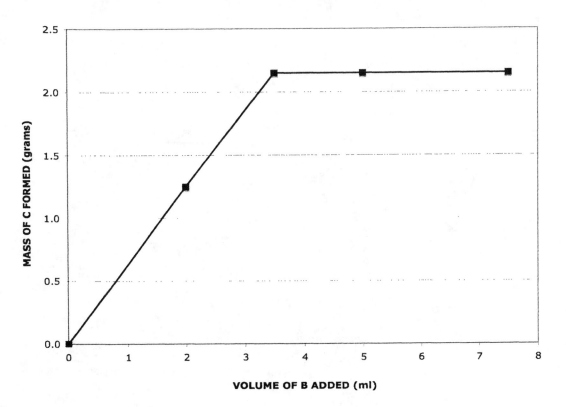

You will notice that some "limiting mass" of product C has formed. Once this mass has been reached (2.15 grams in this example) further addition of B will not lead to any more product forming because the limit has been reached. This is seen as a plateau, or leveling off, of the graph. In your case you may not see the mass actually level off to one distinct value but it should definitely close to within some very narrow range. This is because every measurement you make (the mass from the balance and the volume from the buret) has associated with it some level of uncertainty and these uncertainties affect your final value. So, for example, you may not see a steady final mass of 2.15 grams (as in this demonstration example) but you should see several values "clustered" in a narrow region, say from 2.12 to 2.18 grams.

You will be required to react different amounts of $CaCl_2$ and NaOH, starting with aqueous solutions of each. Both of these solutions are clear and colorless, but when they are mixed the reaction takes place instantly at room temperature and an insoluble white precipitate of $Ca(OH)_2$ is formed. Mixed with the precipitate (but dissolved in the liquid phase) will be the NaCl that is also formed, in addition to any excess NaOH or $CaCl_2$ that may be present. These materials can be washed free of the precipitate and the $Ca(OH)_2$ formed can then be isolated.

We shall determine the amount of each reactant added volumetrically, or based on the volumes of each solution used. Knowing both the concentration and volume of each solution, we can determine the number of moles of each added. Concentration is expressed in molarity (M), which is the number of moles of solute per liter of solution. The solute is the material that is dissolved: in this case it is NaOH and $CaCl_2$. The molarity multiplied by the volume gives the number of moles:

$$Moles \quad = \quad (\text{Volume in liters}) (\text{Molarity}) \qquad (1\text{-}1)$$
$$= \quad (\text{liters})(\text{moles/liter})$$

In this experiment, you will need to use this expression to determine the number of moles of each reactant added to a test tube. Let's use an example to demonstrate how the calculations are done. Suppose you mix together 5.00 ml of 1.0M NaOH and 5.00 ml of 0.75M $CaCl_2$. How much $Ca(OH)_2$ can form? What is the limiting reagent? What is the excess reagent? What is the theoretical yield, in grams, of $Ca(OH)_2$?

$$\text{moles of NaOH} = (1.0 \text{ moles/liter})(0.005 \text{ liter}) = 0.005 \text{ moles NaOH}$$
$$\text{moles of CaCl}_2 = (0.75 \text{ moles/liter})(0.005 \text{ liter}) = 0.00375 \text{ moles CaCl}_2$$

Again, we do the two calculations separately, one based on $CaCl_2$ and one based on NaOH.

$$0.00375 \text{ mol } CaCl_2 \times \frac{1 \text{ mol } Ca(OH)_2}{1 \text{ mol } CaCl_2} = 0.00375 \text{ mol } Ca(OH)_2$$

$$0.005 \text{ mol NaOH} \times \frac{1 \text{ mol } Ca(OH)_2}{2 \text{ mol NaOH}} = 0.0025 \text{ mol } Ca(OH)_2$$

This shows that the limiting reagent is NaOH because it gives the smaller amount of product. Conversely, $CaCl_2$ is the excess reagent. The theoretical yield is always the smaller of the two answers: in this case it is 0.0025 moles of $Ca(OH)_2$. To calculate theoretical yield in grams we need the molar mass of $Ca(OH)_2$:

$$\text{Theoretical yield} = (0.0025 \text{ moles})(74.08 \text{ grams/mole}) = 0.185 \text{ grams}$$

To perform the experiment, you will add specific amounts of both $CaCl_2$ and NaOH to a test tube and allow them to react. To recover the precipitate, you will filter the reaction mixture through a piece of filter paper. By obtaining the mass of the filter paper both before and after the filtration, you can determine the mass of $Ca(OH)_2$ recovered. The precipitate will then be washed with water to remove the NaCl that has also formed (it is water soluble so it will just wash away) and also any excess NaOH or $CaCl_2$ that may still be present. If these impurities are not washed away, they will add to the mass of precipitate you collect and adversely affect your results. Finally, the precipitate will be dried in a microwave oven to remove the water.

While the filter papers are drying in the microwave oven, you will have some free time to try and identify the limiting reagent by a simple chemical test. The clear filtrate that passes through the filter paper will contain water soluble NaCl and any excess $CaCl_2$ or NaOH that may be present. By testing the filtrate separately with both NaOH and $CaCl_2$ we can identify the excess reagent. Consider a filtrate that contains an excess of NaOH. Addition of more NaOH to the filtrate will not cause any change because you are simply increasing the amount of something that is already present but if you add a few drops of $CaCl_2$, it would produce more $Ca(OH)_2$ precipitate. The reverse observations would be noted in case of excess $CaCl_2$. To perform these tests you will need to separate the filtrate into two portions: one for each test. If neither ion is present in excess, then no precipitation will be noted with either reagent.

EXPERIMENTAL PROCEDURE

A. PRECIPITATION REACTION

CAUTION: CONCENTRATED NaOH SOLUTIONS CAN CAUSE SKIN BURNS. IF YOU SPILL ANY ON YOUR HANDS, WASH THEM IMMEDIATELY WITH COOL WATER.

NOTE: It is important that the buret assemblies be left where they are positioned in the lab so other students will have access to them. If you need to refill a buret, pour the solution directly into the top of the buret from a 100 or 150 ml beaker. **DO NOT USE THE PLASTIC FUNNEL BECAUSE IT HOLDS A FAIRLY LARGE VOLUME OF LIQUID AND WILL MOST LIKELY CAUSE A SPILL, WHICH YOU WILL THEN HAVE TO CLEAN UP.**

1. Obtain four funnels, one test tube rack, and eight test tubes from the front bench. Clean the test tubes and funnels with soap and water and then rinse well. They do not need to be dried because you will be dealing with aqueous solutions and the amount of water is unimportant.

2. Label four of the test tubes #1 through #4--the remaining tubes will be used for filtering the precipitate from the mixtures.

3. On the front bench is a dispensing pipet with $CaCl_2$ solution in it. It has been set to deliver 5.00 ml of $CaCl_2$ solution. **DO NOT TOUCH THE ADJUSTMENT SCREW ON THE SIDE OF THE PIPET.** Lift the plunger and then dispense the solution into test tube #1 by depressing the plunger. Repeat this for the other three test tubes.

4. Set up throughout the lab are burets containing 2.50M NaOH solution. Using one of the NaOH solution burets, notice the initial volume in the buret and record it on the data page. When recording volumes, you will notice that the liquid forms a curved surface, called a meniscus, in the buret. To obtain an accurate reading, you need to read the bottom of the meniscus. You will notice that the buret is graduated in 0.1 ml increments. The second decimal place must be estimated from the position of the meniscus. In your mind, imagine the region between two different 0.1 ml graduation marks divided into ten smaller divisions, and estimate the position of the meniscus in these imaginary divisions. When reading the meniscus, look at it at eye level--do not look above or below the meniscus as this leads to an inaccurate reading. Into test tube #1 add about 3 ml of the NaOH solution. The volume need not be exactly 3.00 ml but you must know what the exact volume is. Record the final volume of NaOH in the buret and record it on

the data page. The difference between the two readings is the actual volume of solution transferred to the test tube. The reaction between NaOH and $CaCl_2$ will be instantaneous, forming a white precipitate. Repeat the process for the other three tubes, adding the volume of each solution specified below to each tube.

TUBE NUMBER	VOLUME OF 2.5M NaOH (ml)
1	≈3.00
2	≈4.00
3	≈5.00
4	≈6.00

5. Obtain four pieces of filter paper, number them #1 through #4 to correspond to the reaction mixtures. Using either balance in the front of the lab, determine the mass of each piece of filter paper. Record the respective masses on the data page.

6. Using the technique demonstrated by your instructor, fold filter paper #1 and put it into a funnel. The paper is folded first into halves, then quarters. Once folded, the paper is opened into a cone and placed in the funnel. The number you wrote on the filter paper should be on the outside of the paper ("trapped" between the funnel and the filter paper cone) so that when you remove it from the microwave oven after drying, you will be able to readily identify which of the four papers you are weighing. A few drops of water will help hold the paper in place.

7. Place the stem of the funnel into a clean (rinse it with some water immediately before using it), empty test tube and filter the contents of test tube #1 through the filter paper. If the test tube is contaminated with just a few drops of either NaOH or $CaCl_2$, it could cause the filtrate to appear cloudy and alter your experimental results. You must make sure the test tubes are clean!!! **DO NOT ALLOW THE LIQUID LEVEL TO GO MORE THAN HALFWAY UP THE FILTER PAPER OR THE LIQUID COULD "CREEP" CAUSING SOME OF THE PRECIPITATE TO BE LOST.** Use small amounts of water as necessary to complete the transfer and rinse the precipitate. You must transfer all of the precipitate to the filter paper--the more precipitate you leave in the test tube, the worse your results will be. Remember, we need to determine the mass of precipitate

formed. The liquid that passes through the filter paper, called the filtrate, should be clear. A cloudy filtrate is an indication that the filtration was not successful. This could be due to a hole in the filter paper pouring the reaction mixture so fast that it passes over, and not through, the filter paper. If the filtrate is cloudy, the reaction and filtration will have to be repeated.

8. Pour the clear filtrate back into the test tube (make sure it is clean--rinse it with some water first) you had labeled #1. You will need this filtrate later for testing to determine which is the excess reagent, if one is present.

9. To insure that all of the excess reagent and/or other water-soluble materials have been removed, pass a few small (5 ml or less) portions of distilled water over the precipitate. Test the final drops coming from the funnel with a drop or two of phenolphthalein indicator that can be found in a dropper bottle in the hood. If the filtrate turns pink, it still needs to be washed with additional distilled water. The washing step is not completed until the filtrate gives no color change when phenolphthalein is added. The filtrate from this step can be discarded—it will not be needed later. Remove the filter paper from the funnel and fold the top of the paper over to enclose the precipitate.

10. Repeat the filtering procedure for each of the other three test solutions. You might want to do more than one at a time--this is why you have eight test tubes.

11. Place all four filter papers (still folded) with their precipitates on a paper towel. Place another paper towel on top of the filter papers and apply slight pressure, removing the majority of the water and helping to reduce the drying time.

12. To dry the precipitate we are going to use a microwave oven. Place your samples in the oven and dry it for four minutes on the HIGH setting (or a different time and power setting if indicated by your instructor). This is enough to dry the sample. If there are pockets of excess moisture in your filtered product, it could "pop" in the microwave oven and be distributed all around the inside of the oven, making it much more difficult to collect and weigh.

13. When the samples have dried, obtain a final mass of the filter paper with the precipitate in it. Record the data on the data page. If time permits, put the filter papers back in the microwave oven again and repeat the drying process for about 2 more minutes, then reweigh the filter paper with precipitate. If the precipitate was dried properly, the mass should be the same--this is called heating to constant weight.

B. DETERMINATION OF EXCESS REAGENT

1. Take the filtrate from test tube #1 and divide it into roughly equal portions using another <u>clean</u> test tube. Test one portion by adding <u>a few drops</u> of NaOH solution from the buret. Test the other portion with <u>a few drops</u> of $CaCl_2$ solution. A dropper bottle with $CaCl_2$ solution will be provided for this test. You need only a few drops, not a larger volume. Note any cloudiness, turbidity, or precipitation that forms. Qualitatively indicate a positive or negative reaction on the data page.

2. Repeat the above test on the other three filtrates, each time dividing it into roughly equal portions and testing each portion separately.

3. At the end of your experiment, clean and rinse all of the test tubes with water. Return all test tubes, test tube racks, funnels, wash bottles, and any other equipment you used to the front bench. Clean your work area before you leave.

TREATMENT OF THE DATA

1. For each of the four test mixtures determine the number of moles of both NaOH and $CaCl_2$ added to the test tube using Equation 1-1.

2. Based on the reaction stoichiometry, calculate the maximum amount of $Ca(OH)_2$ that could form-- this is the theoretical yield. Report the theoretical yield in grams of $Ca(OH)_2$.

3. From your test results of Part B, identify the limiting reagent. Support your identification of the limiting reagent with your calculations above.

4. Construct a graph similar to that shown on page 10 by plotting volume of NaOH on the x-axis and the mass of the dried $Ca(OH)_2$ on the y-axis. Notice the correlation between the "plateau" region of the graph and your answers from #2 above.

5. Calculate the percent yield for each reaction:

$$\% \text{ Yield } = \frac{\text{Actual Yield}}{\text{Theoretical Yield}} \times 100\%$$

LABORATORY REPORT

Your laboratory report <u>must</u> consist of the following sections, worth the indicated point values:

Procedure (submitted before lab)	5 points
Cover Page	5 points
Introduction	15 points
Data and Calculations	40 points
Discussion and Conclusions	20 points
Signed Data Page	15 points

A. The Introduction section is to include (in your own words) the theoretical principles behind the experiment and a discussion of what calculations are to be done. It should include the principles involved in the stoichiometric calculations that will be used to reach your final computed value. It is effectively your understanding (but not a direct copy) of the concepts presented in the Background section of this manual.

B. The Data and Calculations section is a recording of the laboratory data from your data page and any calculations requested under "TREATMENT OF DATA". The calculations must be shown in sufficient detail to indicate how the final values were determined.

C. The Discussion and Conclusions section summarizes what you learned from the experiment and should relate to your calculations to support your statements. You should provide explanations for your results here.

THE PROCEDURE MUST BE SUBMITTED BEFORE YOU DO THE EXPERIMENT. FAILURE TO SUBMIT IT ON TIME WILL GIVE NO POINTS FOR THIS SECTION.

NOTE: Your signed data page must be included with your lab report.

DATA PAGE

	#1	#2	#3	#4
Initial Volume of Sodium Hydroxide (ml)				
Final Volume of Sodium Hydroxide (ml)				
Volume of Sodium Hydroxide Delivered (ml)				

	#1	#2	#3	#4
Volume of Calcium Chloride Delivered (ml)				

	#1	#2	#3	#4
Excess Reagent Test with Sodium Hydroxide	either + or −	either + or −	either + or −	either + or −
Excess Reagent Test with Calcium Chloride	either + or −	either + or −	either + or −	either + or −

	#1	#2	#3	#4
Initial Mass of Filter Paper (grams)				
Final Mass of Filter Paper with Precipitate (grams)				
Mass of Precipitate (grams)				

INSTRUCTOR'S SIGNATURE _____   DATE _____

EXPERIMENT #2 - SPECTROSCOPY

OBJECTIVE

In this experiment we are going to observe the spectra (either line or continuous) corresponding to specific electronic transitions in the hydrogen atom, the mercury atom, and several other sources. The Bohr model of atomic structure will be used to determine the orbit numbers associated with the observed spectrum for the hydrogen atom.

BACKGROUND

Spectroscopy is a study of the interaction of electromagnetic radiation with matter. Depending on the radiation we can observe different types of energy transitions within a molecule. For example, microwave radiation tends to cause a molecule to rotate about its bond axes and can give information about bond lengths while infrared radiation tends to cause stretching and bending of the bonds in a molecule. In this experiment, we are going to deal with visible light, which has the effect of promoting electrons to different energy levels.

To understand why and where these transitions occur, we need some background information about atomic structure. One of the early modern theories of atomic structure was the Bohr model in which the electron is theorized to revolve around the nucleus in a fixed orbit much like the planets revolve around the sun. Based largely on the concepts of classical physics about the attractive forces between the electron and proton (remember, they have opposite charges and will therefore be attracted toward each other), Bohr's theory states that the electron can reside in any of several fixed orbits and the energy of any such orbit having an orbit number n is

$$E_n = \frac{-2.179 \times 10^{-18}}{n^2} \text{ joules} \qquad (2\text{-}1)$$

In spectroscopy we measure the amount of energy required to move from one orbit to another. Therefore, we are interested only in energy _differences_, rather than absolute energies. For an electron to move from an initial orbit $n_{initial}$ to a final orbit n_{final}, the energy differences involved are given by the expression:

$$\Delta E = E_{n_{final}} - E_{n_{initial}} \qquad (2\text{-}2)$$

Using equation 2-1 for the energy in any given orbit this expression becomes

$$\Delta E = 2.179 \times 10^{-18} \left[\frac{1}{n_{final}^2} - \frac{1}{n_{initial}^2} \right] joules \qquad (2\text{-}3)$$

You can disregard a negative answer when using this equation because we are actually interested only in the magnitude (and not the sign) of the energy. Each time the value of $n_{initial}$ or n_{final} changes, the energy changes. By irradiating the electron in the hydrogen atom with electromagnetic radiation, it can move to an orbit of higher energy. This is an example of absorption because the electron absorbs some amount of energy and "moves up" from one orbit to another. What orbit it moves to depends on the amount of energy that is absorbed. Planck's contribution to the atomic theory is that energy levels are quantized or can have only fixed values--it is not continuous. The consequence of this on the Bohr model of the atom is that the electron can move only from one orbit to another: it cannot stop between two orbits. For example if the electron starts in the n=1 orbit, it can only move to n=2, n=3, n=4, etc.--it cannot stop halfway between n=1 and n=2. The amount of energy required for absorption (or released by emission) can be related to the frequency (ν) or wavelength (λ) of the electromagnetic radiation involved.

The wavelength is exactly what the name suggests: it is the length of the wave from crest to crest, normally measured in nanometers (abbreviated nm, or 10^{-9} meters). The frequency, on the other hand is a little more difficult to visualize. It is expressed in units of sec^{-1} (1/seconds), which is also called Hertz (Hz). It is best understood by realizing that if you were to stand fixed in one position and count the waves as they pass you, the number of waves that pass you in one second would be the frequency. The energy is related to these quantities through the expression:

$$E = h\nu = \frac{hc}{\lambda} \qquad (2\text{-}4)$$

In this equation, h is Planck's constant (6.626×10^{-34} joule-sec) and c is the speed of light (3.00×10^{17} nm/sec). Note the units on Planck's constant: it is joules multiplied by sec, not joules per second. The single electron in a hydrogen atom is normally found in the n=1 (ground state) orbit. This represents its lowest energy and most stable configuration. This single electron can absorb some quanta of energy and be excited to a higher orbit number. Once it reaches this higher orbit, it tends to rapidly release that energy and return to its more stable n=1 state. This return to its ground state is responsible for the emission lines seen through the spectrometer. Since the radiated light is only of specific energy, these emissions lead to a line spectrum of specific colors. This process is largely the

guiding principle behind a Fourth of July fireworks display. All of the different colors are the result of different elements absorbing energy to raise the electrons to higher orbits. When the electrons relax back to their more stable lower orbits, the energy is released as visible light that you see as a fantastic display of color. Another commonly observed example is salt water boiling over on a stove into a flame. The flame will become colored bright yellow, which corresponds to the line spectrum of the Na atom, present in the salt (NaCl) molecule. In the case of hydrogen, many different lines exist but only a few are observed as visible light. There are different series of lines for hydrogen, each one corresponding to a different value of the final orbit number. In this experiment we are going to measure the wavelength of the lines corresponding to these transitions and convert this to a conclusion regarding the transitions taking place. The different types of transitions for hydrogen are as follows:

FINAL ORBIT NUMBER	RADIATION TYPE	SERIES NAME
n=1	ultraviolet	Lyman
n=2	visible	Balmer
n=3	infrared	Paschen

From this table we see that if the electron returns to n=1 the energy is given off as ultraviolet light that our eyes cannot see. However, some of the electrons will return, if only temporarily, to the n=2 state and the energy released corresponds to visible light that we are going to observe with a spectrometer, then calibrate it so that we can determine the wavelength of the lines that we observe. To achieve this, we are going to standardize the spectrometer using a mercury vapor discharge tube that will show a bright green line at 546 nm. Having standardized the spectrometer, we can observe a hydrogen discharge lamp, note the positions of the lines on the spectrometer, and ultimately figure out what transitions are taking place.

The spectrometer will be used to observe several different light sources. Some sources will be continuous in that they will emit a rainbow of colors while other sources will emit only discrete lines of color. Some may display a combination of these two types.

22

EXPERIMENTAL PROCEDURE

NOTE: PART A (THE CALIBRATION OF THE SPECTROMETER) MUST BE COMPLETED FIRST. AFTER THAT, THE REMAINING SECTIONS CAN BE COMPLETED IN ANY ORDER. IF A LIGHT SOURCE YOU NEED TO USE IS ALREADY OCCUPIED, MOVE ON TO A LATER SECTION AND THEN RETURN TO COMPLETE THE SECTION(S) YOU SKIPPED.

A. CALIBRATION OF THE SPECTROMETER

1. Hold the spectrometer with the print side facing up and look through the diffraction grating (the narrow end). Focus the slit (on the right hand side of the wide end) at the mercury vapor source and observe the positions of the spectral lines. This may take some practice. If you do not focus the slit on the light source, the spectrum you will see will be very weak, or it may be nothing at all if the slit is far away from the light source.

2. You should see a scale with markings to indicate the wavelength in nanometers (nm). You will probably also notice colors at various places inside the spectrometer: this is caused by light entering the spectrometer from different sources. Notice that the plastic disk with the diffraction grating can be rotated. You will notice that the colors will move as you rotate the disk. Rotate the disk until you see the colors in a horizontal line to the left and aligned along the scale.

3. Move the spectrometer around and focus the slit in the general area of the light source until you see a readily visible spectrum. You should see a bright green line that should occur at 546 nm. Notice its position against the scale. If it already occurs at 546 nm, you do not need to do any further calibration. However, if it is not at 546 nm, you need to adjust the spectrometer to bring it into calibration. If an adjustment is necessary, it is to be done on the wide end of the spectrometer. Look at the wider end and notice that the attached diffraction grating has a small hole in it that can be rotated. Using a pen or pencil point, rotate the diffraction grating until the green line occurs at 546 nm. The complete visible spectrum of mercury is shown in Figure 7.7 on page 281 of your course textbook Chemistry: The Molecular Science, Third Edition by John W. Moore, Conrad L. Stanitski, and Peter C. Jurs.

23

B. EMISSION SPECTRUM OF HYDROGEN

1. In the lab will be a discharge tube containing hydrogen. This tube is mounted in a power supply that will cause the electrons in the hydrogen atom to be excited to higher energy levels. As the electrons fall back to their ground state, they emit visible light that you will be able to monitor with your spectrometer. Aim the slit of your spectrometer on the hydrogen discharge tube and observe the lines of the hydrogen spectrum. Note the position and color of each line and record it on the data page. These values will be used to determine the initial orbit number of the electron in the hydrogen atom that causes each line to appear. NOTE: It is possible that you will also see a yellow line at around 580 nm. This is caused by trace amounts of sodium in the glass used to make the discharge tube. As the tube is heated, it is possible that some of the electrons in the sodium could be excited to higher energy levels and cause the emission spectrum of sodium to be seen as the electrons return to their ground state. Disregard this sodium line if you see it: we are only interested in the lines corresponding to hydrogen and there is no yellow line in the hydrogen emission spectrum.

C. EMISSION SPECTRUM OF OTHER GASES

1. In the lab may be discharge tube(s) containing other gases. These tubes are mounted in a power supply that will cause the electrons in the gas atom to be excited to higher energy levels. As the electrons fall back to their ground state, they emit visible light, which you will be able to monitor with your spectrometer. Aim the slit of your spectrometer on the discharge tube and observe the lines of the spectrum. Note the position of each line and record it on the data page. As before, disregard this sodium line if you see it: we are only interested in the lines corresponding to the gas in the tube and there is no yellow line in the emission spectrum of any of the gases we are studying.

D. EMISSION SPECTRUM FROM OTHER SOURCES

1. We are now going to explore sources other than gas discharge tubes. Try aiming the slit of your spectrometer at other light sources to see if a visible spectrum will result. Some possible sources

include: (a) a fluorescent light, (b) an incandescent light such as a 100 watt light bulb, (c) sunlight if it is a clear day, and (d) a burning candle or Bunsen Burner. Also, you could place a small amount of different salts on the tip of a wire and then place the wire in a burner flame. Different salts emit different colors. Some suggestions include sodium chloride, copper chloride, and strontium chloride. If you look at sunlight, you will most likely see a large collection of discrete lines. This is due to the many elements present in sunlight. In fact, the confirmation of the presence of these elements comes from spectral measurements like those you are making. Table 2.1 below lists some of the elements found in sunlight and their respective wavelengths. In some instances, there may be two or more lines so close together (for example, the three lines for magnesium) that the spectrometer will not be able to resolve each line individually so you will only see it as a single (somewhat broader) line

TABLE 2.1 - ABSORPTION LINES IN THE SUN

ELEMENT	WAVELENGTH(S) (nm)
Iron	372.8, 382.0, 430.8, 516.8, 527.0
Calcium	393.4, 396.8
Hydrogen	410.2, 434.0, 486.1, 656.3
Magnesium	516.7, 517.3, 518.4
Sodium	589.0, 590.0
Oxygen	759.4, 762.1

2. Where discrete lines are observed, record their position. If a continuous band is noted instead of a series of lines, record the position of the beginning and end of the band. At the end of your experiment, return all equipment and clean up your work area.

TREATMENT OF THE DATA

1. Using your data from Section B, note the wavelength of each line observed in the hydrogen spectrum. Convert these wavelengths into their respective energies using:

$$E = \frac{hc}{\lambda}$$

Compare your data with the complete visible spectrum of hydrogen, which is shown in Figure 7.8 on page 282 of your course textbook Chemistry: The Molecular Science, Third Edition by John W. Moore, Conrad L. Stanitski, and Peter C. Jurs. The lines that you see actually arise from changes in orbit number, so they are really the value of ΔE that you will use in Step #2.

2. Recognizing that all of the lines of the hydrogen spectrum that lie in the visible region terminate with $n_{final} = 2$, calculate the initial orbit number, $n_{initial}$, for the Bohr model using Equation 2-3.

3. For all other lines noted in Sections C and D, tabulate (a) the wavelength, (b) the frequency, and (c) the energy associated with each emission. For any continuous band(s) noted, tabulate each color and the "range" of wavelengths it includes. There are no orbit number calculations for any spectrum other than hydrogen.

LABORATORY REPORT

Your laboratory report must consist of the following sections, worth the indicated point values:

Procedure (submitted before lab)	5 points
Cover Page	5 points
Introduction	15 points
Data and Calculations	40 points
Observations/Discussion/Conclusions	20 points
Signed Data Page	15 points

A. The Introduction section must include a brief discussion of the process of emission and absorption of radiation. The Bohr model of the atom must be correlated to the measurements made in the experiment. All equations used in the treatment of data must be identified. It is effectively your understanding (but not a direct copy) of the concepts presented in the Background section of this manual.

B. The Experimental Data and Calculations section is composed of all data recorded on the data sheet and all of the calculations requested in the TREATMENT OF DATA section. Calculations should be done in sufficient detail using units where appropriate to indicate your level of understanding. Because of the number of calculations necessary, this segment is worth a large percentage of the report grade.

C. Observations are primarily the colors of the specific transitions observed. Conclusions and Discussions are primarily the distinction between line spectra and continuous spectra and must reflect back to your data and experimental results. Comment on the applicability of the measurements made to the values expected based on the Bohr model of the atom. You should provide explanations for your results here.

THE PROCEDURE MUST BE SUBMITTED BEFORE YOU DO THE EXPERIMENT. FAILURE TO SUBMIT IT ON TIME WILL GIVE NO POINTS FOR THIS SECTION.

NOTE: Your signed data page must be included with your lab report.

DATA PAGE

PART B - EMISSION SPECTRUM OF HYDROGEN

COLOR OF LINE NOTED	WAVELENGTH (nm)
_____	_____
_____	_____
_____	_____
_____	_____

PART C - EMISSION SPECTRUM FROM OTHER GASES

Type of tube used_____

COLOR OF LINE NOTED	WAVELENGTH (nm)
_____	_____
_____	_____
_____	_____
_____	_____
_____	_____

Type of tube used_____

COLOR OF LINE NOTED	WAVELENGTH (nm)
_____	_____
_____	_____
_____	_____
_____	_____
_____	_____

28

PART D - EMISSION SPECTRUM FROM OTHER SOURCES

1. LINE SPECTRUM

Type of source used_____

COLOR OF LINE NOTED	WAVELENGTH (nm)
_____	_____
_____	_____
_____	_____
_____	_____

Type of source used_____

COLOR OF LINE NOTED	WAVELENGTH (nm)
_____	_____
_____	_____
_____	_____

2. CONTINUOUS SPECTRUM

Type of source used_____

COLOR OF BAND NOTED	WAVELENGTH (nm)
Blue	_____
Orange	_____
Green	_____
Red	_____

INSTRUCTOR'S SIGNATURE_____   DATE_____

29

EXPERIMENT #3 - CONDUCTIVITY OF SOLUTIONS

OBJECTIVE

This experiment is designed to show the differences between ionic and molecular compounds as determined by a measure of their conductivity. There are two primary objectives of the experiment. The first is semi-quantitative in which a rough separation based on "low" and "high" conductivity values will enable us to separate compounds as being either ionic or molecular. The second part is a more quantitative study in which the effect of both the concentration and number of ions will be evaluated. Data for the first part will be recorded manually, while the data for the second part will be collected using a computer-assisted method incorporating the Vernier LoggerPro System.

BACKGROUND

All chemical compounds can be classified as being either ionic or molecular (sometimes also called covalent) based on their properties. Table 3.1 below gives some of the typical properties of each type. A more detailed discussion of the similarities and differences can be found in Sections 3.1 (pages 79 to 82), 3.5 (pages 89 to 95), and 3.7 (pages 98 to 101) in your course textbook, Chemistry: The Molecular Science, Third Edition by John W. Moore, Conrad L. Stanitski, and Peter C. Jurs.

TABLE 3.1 - PROPERTIES OF IONIC AND MOLECULAR COMPOUNDS

MOLECULAR COMPOUNDS	IONIC COMPOUNDS
mostly nonmetals with nonmetals	metals with nonmetals
gases, liquids, or solids	mostly crystalline solids
brittle, weak, and/or soft	hard, brittle solids
low melting points	high melting points
low boiling points	high boiling points
poor conductors of heat and electricity	good conductors of heat and electricity
many insoluble in water	many soluble in water

30

The characteristic we are going to focus on in this experiment is the ability to conduct electricity. When an ionic compound dissolves in water it, dissociates, or fragments, into charged species called ions. These ions enable the solution to conduct electricity. When this happens, an electrical circuit is completed across the electrodes of a conductivity probe, and a numerical measure of the conductivity is possible. When the value of the conductivity is "high", the solution is termed an electrolyte. For example, when common table salt (NaCl) is dissolved in water, it completely dissociates into Na^+ and Cl^- ions. It is these ions in solution that give the observed conductivity:

$$NaCl_{(s)} \quad \rightarrow \quad Na^+_{(aq)} \quad + \quad Cl^-_{(aq)}$$

Molecular compounds, for the most part, do not dissociate into charged species but rather remain as intact molecules. Because of this, they do not conduct electricity to any appreciable extent. There is normally some slight residual conductivity from distilled water because it naturally contains a very low concentration of H^+ and OH^- ions (we'll study this in more detail in CHEM 102). When the value of the conductivity is "very low", the solution is termed a nonelectrolyte. An example of this is ethanol (grain alcohol), which simply dissolves and does not dissociate:

$$C_2H_5OH_{(l)} \quad \rightarrow \quad C_2H_5OH_{(aq)}$$

Therefore, based on a measurement of conductivity, we can make a rough separation as to class of compound, either ionic or molecular.

While these examples define the two extremes of behavior, there are some compounds that give "not too low" but "not too high" conductivity. They are essentially a "middle ground" in these two classes of compounds. An example of this is household ammonia (a solution of NH_3 in water), which is partially dissociated:

$$NH_{3(g)} \quad + \quad H_2O_{(l)} \quad \leftrightarrows \quad NH_4^+_{(aq)} \quad + \quad OH^-_{(aq)}$$

This is an example of a chemical equilibrium condition (indicated by the arrow going in both directions), which we shall discuss in more detail in CHEM 102. In this case, the reaction goes to less than about 5% completion, so it is termed a weak electrolyte. Therefore, we can use conductivity to categorize compounds into categories: (a) strong electrolytes, which completely dissociate and give high conductivity, (b) nonelectrolytes, which dissolve, do not dissociate, and show very low conductivity, and (c) weak electrolytes, which dissociate "a little bit" but not enough to give a high conductivity. In Part A of this experiment, we are going to investigate a series of aqueous solutions

(water is the solvent) of various types. Each solution will have the same concentration, so the effect of concentration will not play a role: we'll study that effect in Part B. Based on the value of the conductivity you record, you will then assign each compound to one of the three classes listed above.

Since conductivity is roughly a measure of the concentration of ions in solution, it is logical to expect that higher concentrations should yield higher conductivity. A point that may not seem quite as obvious is the effect, if any, from ionic charge. That is, does an ion having a +1 (or -1) charge have as much of an impact as an ion of +3 (or -3) charge at the same concentration, or do all ions behave the same regardless of charge? Different charges mean different stoichiometry, which may affect the conductivity. For example a 1.0M solution of the electrolyte KCl would dissociate to give 1.0M of K^+ and also 1.0M of Cl^-, so the effective "total ion concentration" is 2.0M. On the other hand, a 1.0M solution of an electrolyte such as $MgCl_2$ would give a different total ion concentration. When it dissociates, there are two Cl^- ions for each Mg^{+2} ion, so now the "total ion concentration" would be 3.0M. What impact does this have? Does the fact that the charges are +2 and -1 make a difference compared to +1 and -1? This will be explored in Part B, in which we shall start with pure water (which will have a very low conductivity) and then add a specified number of drops of different materials, each at a concentration of 1.0M. One will be a nonelectrolyte (molecular compound), a second will be NaCl (an electrolyte with a +1 and a -1 ion), a third will be $CaCl_2$ (an electrolyte with a +2 and two -1 ions) , and then finally $AlCl_3$ (an electrolyte with a +3 and three -1 ions). By measuring the conductivity of each one and then constructing a plot of conductivity as a function of the number of drops added, we shall see the effect, if any, that ionic charge has on conductivity. Mathematically, evaluating the slope of each straight line generated will show the effect of the charges: the larger the slope, the greater the impact. This part of the experiment will be done by using the Vernier LoggerPro system to collect data and store it in data files. Prior to leaving the lab you can the email the data file to yourself or copy it from the laptop computer and take it with you. When writing your lab report, you will open this data file and construct the necessary graphs. By plotting the graph for each of the four compounds within the same set of axes (essentially overlaying all of the graphs) the effect of ionic charge will become apparent.

32

EXPERIMENTAL PROCEDURE

A - CLASSES OF COMPOUNDS

1. The laptop will already be set up for you when you arrive at the lab. Set the switch on the conductivity probe for the 0-20000 range (the uppermost position). On the desktop you will find an icon labeled **CONDUCTIVITY (A)**. Double click on the icon to open the application. When it has opened, the desktop will show a large display of the numerical value of the conductivity. The standard unit of conductivity is the mho/cm, which is now more commonly referred to as siemen/cm. To keep the magnitude of the numerical values more "reasonable" the display is expressed in microsiemens/cm (μS/cm). In Part A, you will manually record the conductivity on your data page.

2. Into a small test tube place enough <u>distilled</u> water to fill the tube about 1/4 of the way. When the conductivity probe is placed in the tube, the liquid level will rise and cover the sensor, which is located in the hole at the bottom of the probe. When the value of the conductivity has stabilized, record it on the data page. Ideally, distilled water should show a conductivity of zero, but there is normally some small residual value due to minute amounts of H^+ and OH^- ions that naturally occur in pure water.

3. Empty the distilled water from the test tube and replace it with a similar amount of 0.05M CH_3OH. NOTE: There are two CH_3OH solutions stored on the front bench. In this part you want the 0.05M solution (stored in a plastic squeeze bottle) and not the 1.0M solution stored in the clear glass bottle. The more concentrated solution will be used in Part B. Before testing this solution, clean the probe by rinsing it with a small amount of distilled water from a wash bottle. Blot the outside of the probe end with a paper towel. It is <u>not</u> necessary to dry the <u>inside</u> of the hole near the probe.

4. Measure the conductivity of the 0.05M CH_3OH solution and then record its value on the data page when it has stabilized.

5. Repeat this procedure for each of the solutions listed on the data page, making sure to properly rinse the probe between each solution to prevent contamination from the previous solution.

6. Just for comparison sake, also measure the conductivity of tap water and compare it to the value you observed for distilled water. This should show why distilled water is used to make each of the solutions and also why it serves as a "control".

33

7. When the last solution has been tested, close the application by selecting **EXIT** from the **FILE** menu, or just select **ALT** plus **F4**. If you are asked if you want to save any changes, select **NO**, so it will be ready for the next class.

B - EFFECT OF CONCENTRATION

1. Change the switch on the conductivity probe to the 0-2000 range (the lower position). On the desktop you will find an icon labeled **CONDUCTIVITY (B)**. Double click on the icon to open the application. When it has opened, the desktop will show both a graph and a data table to the left of the graph. The table will have columns to record Volume (in drops) and the Conductivity (in μS/cm). There will also be a display of the conductivity directly beneath the two columns. In Part B, the computer will record the data.

2. Obtain a plastic pipet and place in it some 1.0M CH_3OH solution that is stored on the front bench. NOTE: you only need a small amount of solution for this part. Withdraw a small amount directly into a plastic pipet: **do not** pour the solution into a beaker to take a sample.

3. Add about 70 ml of <u>distilled</u> water (remember: we found out in Part A why distilled water must be used) to a <u>clean</u> 100 ml beaker. Click **COLLECT** at the top of the screen. Using the probe, stir the contents of the beaker for a few seconds and then leave the probe sit undisturbed in the beaker.

4. When the conductivity reading has stabilized, click **KEEP** and then enter **0** in the edit box (indicating that zero drops of the CH_3OH have been added). Press the **ENTER** key to store this data pair. This gives the conductivity of the water before anything has been added to it.

5. Add 1 drop of the 1.0M CH_3OH solution, use the probe to stir the solution, and then repeat Step #4, this time entering **1** (the total number of drops of CH_3OH added) in the edit box and press **ENTER**. Repeat this procedure until a total of eight drops have been added. Each time, the value to enter is the TOTAL number of drops of 1.0 M CH_3OH that have been added to the beaker.

6. Click **STOP** when you have finished collecting data. To save the data file to the desktop, select **EXPORT AS TEXT** from the **FILE** menu and give the file a name. Since this was done by adding CH_3OH to the distilled water, you may as well just call it CH_3OH.

34

7. Select **CLEAR ALL DATA** from the **DATA** menu. Don't worry: all of your data were saved to the desktop in Step #6.

8. Now we want to repeat this study using other materials in place of 1.0M CH$_3$OH. Starting with a new, clean, plastic pipet (throw the old one away to prevent contamination), repeat Steps 2 through 7 using 1.0M NaCl, then 1.0M CaCl$_2$, and finally 1.0M AlCl$_3$.

9. When you have collected data for all four samples, go to the **FILE** menu and select **EXIT**, or just select **ALT** plus **F4**. You will be asked if you want to save the changes made to **CONDUCTIVITY (B)**. Select **NO,** so it will be all set up for the next class. All of the data have already been saved in their own respective files.

10. When you return to the desktop, you will see your four data files there, identified by the names you assigned. You will need these files to complete your lab report. You can email them to yourself. The PC is equipped with a wireless Internet card, and you can email the necessary files from the lab. Alternatively, you can also transfer them to a USB Flash Drive if you prefer. CAUTION: The computer is already set up for the appropriate wireless connection network. If you try to change to a different one, chances are very good that it will not work properly. DO NOT CHANGE THE WIRELESS NETWORK SETTING.

11. After you have transferred your data files, move them to the recycle bin and then delete them from the system. Your instructor will not sign your data sheet until each of these steps has been completed.

TREATMENT OF THE DATA

1. Using the numerical conductivities you recorded on the data page, line them up in order of increasing (lowest to highest) values. Based on the magnitude of those values, assign each solution to one of three categories: (a) strong electrolytes (which are the ionic compounds), (b) nonelectrolytes (which are the molecular compounds), or (c) weak electrolytes (those that show an equilibrium condition).

2. To interpret the data in Part B, a more mathematically based treatment is needed. Open any one of your four data files using an application that can be used to graph the data, such as Microsoft Excel. Prepare a graph of the data by plotting conductivity on the y-axis and the total number of

drops on the x-axis. <u>By the method of linear regression using all of the data</u>, determine the slope of the best straight line through the points: this will be the determining factor in making your conclusion. Repeat this process for each of the other three data files. You might find it more convenient to plot all four graphs within the same set of axes (as overlays). By doing this, you will have a single picture that shows all of the data simultaneously.

3.   From your data in Part B, rank the materials tested in increasing (lowest to highest) impact on conductivity. The slope will help you do this. Since the slope is the change in y axis (the change in conductivity) relative to the change in the x axis (the change in the number of drops), the larger the value of the slope, the larger is the impact. From this you should be able to conclude what effect, if any, the total ionic concentration of the solution has on the conductivity.

36

LABORATORY REPORT

Your laboratory report <u>must</u> consist of the following sections, worth the indicated point values:

Procedure (submitted before lab)	5 points
Cover Page	5 points
Introduction	15 points
Experimental Data and Graphs	45 points
Conclusions and Discussion	15 points
Signed Data Page	15 points

A. The Introduction must contain a discussion about the similarities and differences between ionic and molecular compounds. Specifically include a discussion about the differences in conductivity of each type. Also make sure to indicate the three categories that will be used to classify the types of solutions studied. The effect of concentration and/or charge on the measured conductivity must also be considered. It is effectively your understanding (but not a direct copy) of the concepts presented in the Background section of this manual.

B. The Experimental Data and Graphs section must contain all of the calculations listed in the TREATMENT OF THE DATA section. Also, it is to contain a printout of all of your raw data and the graph for each solution studied in Part B.

C. Conclusions/Discussions must reflect back to your data and experimental results. You should provide explanations for your results here.

THE PROCEDURE MUST BE SUBMITTED BEFORE YOU DO THE EXPERIMENT. FAILURE TO SUBMIT IT ON TIME WILL GIVE NO POINTS FOR THIS SECTION.

NOTE: Your signed data page must be included with your lab report.

37

DATA PAGE

NAME_____ SECTION_____ DATE_____

PART A - CLASSES OF COMPOUNDS

SOLUTION	CONDUCTIVITY (μS/cm)
Distilled Water	_____
0.05M CH_3OH	_____
0.05M $C_2H_6O_2$	_____
0.05M H_3BO_3	_____
0.05M CH_3COOH	_____
0.05M KBr	_____
0.05M HCl	_____
Tap Water	_____

INSTRUCTOR'S SIGNATURE_____ DATE_____

EXPERIMENT #4 - DETERMINATION OF MOLAR MASS BY FREEZING POINT DEPRESSION

OBJECTIVE

This experiment is designed to demonstrate the application of one of the colligative properties of a solution. By measuring the change in freezing point of both a pure solvent and also a solution made from that same solvent, the difference will be used as a basis for determining the molar mass.

BACKGROUND

A fundamental characteristic property of a substance that can be used as an aid in its identification is its freezing, or melting, point which is a constant value for any material and is independent of the amount present. For example, water freezes (melts) at 0°C regardless of whether you consider a small ice cube added to a drink or an iceberg as big as the one that sank the Titanic. All solutions are composed of at least two components: a solvent and one or more solutes. The solvent is present in the major amount and the solute(s) is/are the minor component(s). When a solute is dissolved in a solvent, the freezing point, T_f, of the resulting solution is lower than that of the pure solvent. The magnitude of the freezing point depression, ΔT_f, depends on the amount of solute dissolved and is given by the expression

$$\Delta T_f = k_f \, m \qquad (4\text{-}1)$$

where m is the molality of solute in the solution and k_f is a constant characteristic of the <u>solvent</u> called the molal freezing point depression constant. The molality is the number of moles of <u>solute</u> dissolved per kilogram of solvent. Given the value of k_f, and then experimentally measuring ΔT_f, we can readily determine the molality of solute in any given solution:

$$m = \frac{\Delta T_f}{k_f} \qquad (4\text{-}2)$$

From this, we can then determine how many moles of solute were present in our solution based on the kg of solvent used:

$$\text{moles of solute} = (\text{molality})(\text{kg of solvent used}) \qquad (4\text{-}3)$$

Knowing the moles of solute present, in addition to how many grams of solute were added to the solution, we can determine the molar mass of the solute

$$\text{Molar Mass} = \frac{\text{grams of solute added}}{\text{moles of solute}} \qquad (4\text{-}4)$$

The freezing point can be determined by cooling the sample in an ice bath and then monitoring the temperature as a function of time. When the data are graphed with the x-axis being the time and the y-axis being the temperature, a cooling curve results. At the freezing point you will notice that the temperature remains constant while the liquid freezes, resulting in a plateau on the curve. A typical example of a cooling curve is shown below. In this case, there are two curves on the same set of axes: one is for the pure solvent and the other is for the solution. You will notice that the plateau for the solution is at a lower temperature because the freezing point has been depressed. The difference in the freezing points as taken from these curves is the ΔT_f value you will need to use to determine molar mass.

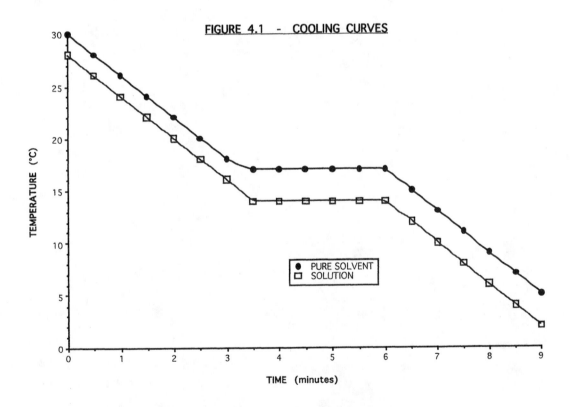

FIGURE 4.1 - COOLING CURVES

In this experiment we are going to use cyclohexanol as the solvent. This is because it has a conveniently measured freezing point (near room temperature) and it also has a very favorable value

of k_f (39.4°C/m). First we measure the freezing point of a known amount of pure cyclohexanol to serve as a starting point. Next, an accurately measured amount of a solute is added to the cyclohexanol and dissolved to give a homogeneous solution. The solute will be one of the following compounds. The molar mass of each is given for reference.

Tetradecanol (214.4 grams/mol)

Hexadecanol (242.5 grams/mol)

Octadecanol (270.5 grams/mol)

The freezing point of this solution is then measured in the same fashion as for the pure cyclohexanol. The difference in these two freezing points is the ΔT_f value needed to do the calculations. The concept of freezing point lowering is discussed on pages 748 through 750 of your course textbook, Chemistry: The Molecular Science, Third Edition by John W. Moore, Conrad L. Stanitski, and Peter C. Jurs.

EXPERIMENTAL PROCEDURE

1. Obtain a test tube, thermometer, and a 250 ml beaker from the front bench. Clean and thoroughly dry the test tube if necessary. Small amounts of water left in the test tube will function as a solute, effectively depressing the freezing point of the cycohexanol and altering your data.

2. Cyclohexanol will be stored in a plastic squeeze bottle and most likely will be kept in a hot water bath in the fume hood. This is because it freezes very close to room temperature. Place the test tube inside a beaker, tare the balance display, and then add cyclohexanol to the test tube until there is between 9 and 10 grams of cyclohexanol in it. Record the exact mass to the nearest 0.01 gram and enter it on your data page.

3. Insert the thermometer in the test tube, then place it in one of the hot water baths stored in the fume hood. Allow the cyclohexanol to warm to at least 35°C.

4. Remove the test tube from the water bath and place it in the beaker. Add enough water to fill the beaker about halfway and then add some ice to the beaker (a small handful should be adequate). CAUTION: Do not add so much ice that the water level is near the neck of the test tube. If water accidentally gets inside the tube it will depress the freezing point of the cyclohexanol. If you use too much ice, the sample may cool too quickly and you may miss the freezing point.

41

5. Record the temperature of the cyclohexanol every 10 seconds and enter it on the data page. **NOTE: It is very important to use the thermometer to stir the contents of the test tube between readings. Failure to do this can cause temperature gradients in the sample and seriously affect your results.** The temperatures you record will give you a value of ΔT_f, which will ultimately be used to determine the molar mass of the solute and lead to the conclusion of which solute you used. These values are crucial to making your conclusion so it is important to record them as accurately as possible. You will notice that the thermometers are graduated in 1°C increments. To obtain maximum accuracy, you will have to estimate the temperature to the nearest 0.2°C. When you reach the freezing point the temperature will remain constant. This occurs on the plateau of the cooling curve as shown on page 39. NOTE: If you find that the plateau occurs at just a few degrees above zero, then your sample probably cooled too quickly and you missed the freezing point. If that happens, repeat the process starting with Step #3 above.

6. Place the test tube containing the cyclohexanol back in the hot water bath in the fume hood. While the cyclohexanol is melting, place about 0.7 to 0.8 grams (weighed to the nearest 0.01 gram) of your unknown solute on to a piece of weighing paper. Record both the mass and the code number of the solute on the data page. CAUTION: Adding too much solute can cause the freezing point to be depressed by so much that you might not be able to get the solution to freeze. This is the substance whose molar mass we are trying to determine. Add the solute to the test tube containing the cyclohexanol. The solute will not completely dissolve at first to form a homogeneous solution. Leave the test tube back in the hot water bath in the fume hood until the solute melts. Once it has melted it will dissolve very easily to form a single phase. WHEN THE TEMPERATURE DROPS BELOW THE MELTING POINT OF THE SOLUTE, IT WILL NOT PRECIPITATE FROM THE SOLUTION. Repeat Steps #4 and #5 on this solution. NOTE: Since this solution must have a freezing point below that of the pure cyclohexanol, don't bother recording any data until the temperature is about 4 or 5° above what you found for the pure cyclohexanol. For example, if you found the freezing point of pure cyclohexanol to be 24°C, it is not necessary to record any temperatures for the mixture until it has dropped to about 28°C. **For the mixture it is very important to stir the contents of the test tube between readings.** The designation of "zero time" is arbitrary and will not affect the data at all. This will reduce the number of non-useful data points and should make constructing the graphs a bit easier.

42

7. When the sample has frozen, remove it from the water bath, once again melt the contents of the test tube and then dispose of the sample in the containers designated for disposal that can be found in the fume hood.

8. Rinse the test tube several times with water to clean it, dry it, and then return all of your equipment to the front bench.

TREATMENT OF THE DATA

1. Using the data for the pure cyclohexanol, construct a cooling curve by plotting time on the x-axis and temperature on the y-axis. Identify the freezing point, which will be the temperature where the plateau in the graph occurs.

2. Construct another graph, this time using the data for the solution containing the dissolved solute. Place both graphs on the same set of axes (as shown in Figure 4.1) to more easily see the difference in the freezing points. The difference in the two values is ΔT_f. It will be easier (and much more accurate) to determine this from your written data rather than trying to estimate it from the graph. Sometimes there is not a well-defined plateau with the solution. If this happens, the temperature you want to record as the freezing point is where the successive difference between two data points is the smallest. In an ideal situation this difference is zero (giving the plateau), but sometimes the smallest difference is only about 0.2 or 0.3°C because as a mixture freezes the composition constantly changes. You would notice the same thing if you freeze a soft drink then let it defrost. As it thaws, the initial liquid that forms has most of the flavoring from the drink and the taste seems exceptionally "strong".

3. Using your experimental value of ΔT_f and the k_f for cyclohexanol (which is 39.4°C/m), calculate the molality of the solute using Equation 4-2. An example of these calculations can be found in Problem Solving Example 15.12 on page 750 of your course textbook, Chemistry: The Molecular Science, Third Edition by John W. Moore, Conrad L. Stanitski, and Peter C. Jurs.

4. Recognizing that you used much less than 1.0 kg of solvent, calculate the number of moles of solute present in your solution using Equation 4-3. Don't forget to first convert your mass of cyclohexanol (which you recorded in grams) into kilograms.

43

5. Since the molar mass is given in units of grams/mol, use your experimental mass of solute added and the number of moles calculated in Step #4 to determine the molar mass of the solute using Equation 4-4. From your experimental molar mass, determine which of the solutes listed on page 40 is the one you used.

LABORATORY REPORT

Your laboratory report must consist of the following sections, worth the indicated point values:

Procedure (submitted before lab)	5 points
Cover Page	5 points
Introduction	15 points
Experimental Data and Graphs	40 points
Conclusions and Discussion	20 points
Signed Data Page	15 points

A. The Introduction must contain a discussion about the concept of freezing point depression as a colligative property of solutions. Specifically include a discussion about the effect of the amount of dissolved solute on the change in the freezing point and how this will be used to determine molar mass. It is effectively your understanding (but not a direct copy) of the concepts presented in the Background section of this manual.

B. The Experimental Data and Graphs section must contain all of the calculations listed in the TREATMENT OF THE DATA section, including the cooling curves for both the pure cyclohexanol and the solution.

C. Conclusions/Discussions must reflect back to your data and experimental results. It must also include the identity of your unknown (from the three listed on page 40) based on your experimental results.

THE PROCEDURE MUST BE SUBMITTED BEFORE YOU DO THE EXPERIMENT. FAILURE TO SUBMIT IT ON TIME WILL GIVE NO POINTS FOR THIS SECTION.

NOTE: Your signed data page must be included with your lab report.

44

DATA PAGE

Mass of cyclohexanol _____ grams

TIME (seconds)	TEMPERATURE (°C)	TIME (seconds)	TEMPERATURE (°C)
_____	_____	_____	_____
_____	_____	_____	_____
_____	_____	_____	_____
_____	_____	_____	_____
_____	_____	_____	_____
_____	_____	_____	_____
_____	_____	_____	_____
_____	_____	_____	_____
_____	_____	_____	_____
_____	_____	_____	_____
_____	_____	_____	_____
_____	_____	_____	_____
_____	_____	_____	_____
_____	_____	_____	_____
_____	_____	_____	_____
_____	_____	_____	_____
_____	_____	_____	_____
_____	_____	_____	_____
_____	_____	_____	_____
_____	_____	_____	_____
_____	_____	_____	_____
_____	_____	_____	_____

45

Mass of solute added to cyclohexanol _____ grams

Code Number of Solute Used _____

TIME (seconds)	TEMPERATURE (°C)	TIME (seconds)	TEMPERATURE (°C)
_____	_____	_____	_____
_____	_____	_____	_____
_____	_____	_____	_____
_____	_____	_____	_____
_____	_____	_____	_____
_____	_____	_____	_____
_____	_____	_____	_____
_____	_____	_____	_____
_____	_____	_____	_____
_____	_____	_____	_____
_____	_____	_____	_____
_____	_____	_____	_____
_____	_____	_____	_____
_____	_____	_____	_____
_____	_____	_____	_____
_____	_____	_____	_____
_____	_____	_____	_____
_____	_____	_____	_____
_____	_____	_____	_____
_____	_____	_____	_____
_____	_____	_____	_____

INSTRUCTOR'S SIGNATURE_____   DATE_____

46

EXPERIMENT #5 - PREPARATION OF AN ESTER

OBJECTIVE

This experiment is somewhat different from many others in this manual because it deals with synthesis, or the manufacture of a product, and the primary emphasis is obtaining a specific product. The mass of each reactant used will then be used in a stoichiometry calculation to help support or verify your conclusion.

INTRODUCTION

Esters are a class of molecules that have widespread industrial importance. The simple esters are generally quite fragrant and are the source of the aroma and/or flavor of many different fruits. They are also found in scents such as those used to make air fresheners or they can be added to paraffin wax to make scented candles. Drinks that are labeled to contain "artificial flavoring" generally have a blend of different esters that all combine to give the desired scent or flavor. By using esters, a food can be given a particular flavor without containing any of that item. An example is rum flavoring added to ice cream and desserts like puddings. By using a combination of esters, it can be given the flavor and aroma of rum but not contain any rum at all!!! Some esters are also excellent lubricants and some synthetic motor oils are ester based. They can be made by heating a mixture of an alcohol (R-OH) with a carboxylic acid (R'-COOH). When writing reactions between different functional groups, it is best to have the functionalities "face each other" so the reaction becomes more apparent. In ester synthesis, the -H of the alcohol functionality chemically combines with -OH from the carboxylic acid to make H_2O. The two fragments are then "hooked together" at the point of reaction and the ester structure is determined. The general reaction is:

$$R\text{-}O\boxed{H \ + \ HO}C\text{-}R' \quad \underset{OH^-}{\overset{H^+}{\rightleftharpoons}} \quad R'\text{-}C\text{-}O\text{-}R \ + \ H\text{-}OH$$

47

The R groups represent alkyl groups that may be the same or different: that is why they have been designated as R and R'. In the case of the alcohol, the R group must contain at least one carbon atom: if the R group were a H atom it would be water, which does not have the chemical characteristics of an alcohol. In the case of the carboxylic acid, the R' group can be a H atom but it generally contains at least one carbon atom. The double arrow separating reactants and products indicates a state of chemical equilibrium exists. The H^+ above the forward arrow indicates that an acid catalyst will help speed up the reaction, while the OH^- below the reverse arrow indicates that a base catalyst will help speed up that reaction. It is the reversibility of this reaction that can also limit the use of some esters in specific applications. For example, esters are rarely used as a contributor to fragrance in better quality colognes and perfumes. Fragrant hydrocarbons, ketones, and/or ethers extracted from natural sources are used instead because human sweat in contact with some esters can cause hydrolysis of the ester, generating an alcohol and a carboxylic acid. Most carboxylic acids have unpleasant odors: acetic (ethanoic) acid has the odor of vinegar and butyric (butanoic) acid has the odor of rancid butter, of which it is an ingredient. Unless steps can be taken to significantly reduce or completely eliminate hydrolysis, esters based on these acids would contribute seriously to "body odor".

We mentioned earlier that esters generally have pleasant fragrances and Table 5.1 lists a few common simple esters, along with the alcohol and carboxylic acid needed to make them. The ester you will be assigned to make in this experiment will be taken from this list. Based on the odor you detect, you will then have to identify the ester you made and both the acid and alcohol used to make it. For the carboxylic acids, the IUPAC name is given first, with the common name listed next to it in parentheses. For the alcohols the common name is given in the table and the common names are also used for the esters. For example, the ester that gives the odor of wintergreen is methyl salicylate, which is derived from methyl alcohol and salicylic acid. The esters of common industrial and practical importance have been known for so long, for many years before the IUPAC naming system was in place, that the common names are still used today in preference to the IUPAC names. As you can see from this list, their appearance in common items is quite varied and if in fact we were making all of these esters at the same time, the lab would have an aroma resembling that of a "fruit store". For a chemistry lab, normally thought of as an area filled with foul smells, that's not too bad!!

48

TABLE 5.1 - SOME COMMON SIMPLE ESTERS

CARBOXYLIC ACID	ALCOHOL	NAME OF ESTER	SOURCE OR USE
anthranilic	methyl	methyl anthranilate	grapes
cinnamic	methyl	methyl cinnamate	strawberry
cinnamic	ethyl	ethyl cinnamate	cinnamon
acetic	ethyl	ethyl acetate	nail polish remover
acetic	isoamyl	isoamyl acetate	bananas
acetic	n-octyl	octyl acetate	oranges
acetic	n-propyl	propyl acetate	pears
salicylic	methyl	methyl salicylate	oil of wintergreen
propionic	isobutyl	isobutyl propionate	rum

EXPERIMENTAL PROCEDURE

CAUTION: IN THIS EXPERIMENT WE ARE GOING TO USE A HOT SOLUTION OF H_2SO_4 WHICH CAN CAUSE SERIOUS SKIN BURNS. BE SURE TO USE EXTREME CARE IN ITS USE, FOLLOWING YOUR LAB INSTRUCTOR'S DIRECTIONS CAREFULLY.

1. From the front bench, obtain one Erlenmeyer flask and two test tubes that can fit into the neck of the flask. Also, one member of your group will need to exchange their I.D. card for a magnetic stir bar. The I.D. card will be returned when the magnetic stir bar is returned.

2. First you need to prepare two cold finger condensers that will be used to reflux the reaction mixture and prevent it from escaping. They are made from the test tubes. Approximately the lower third of the test tube should fit in the neck of the Erlenmeyer flask without falling in. If the base of the test tube is not wide enough, it can be "built up" by wrapping tape around it. NOTE: The tape should be applied to roughly the midpoint of the test tube to prevent it from actually touching the reaction mixture. Filling the test tube with ice chips and inserting it into the neck of the Erlenmeyer flask make the condenser.

3. In the fume hoods you will find bottles labeled as "Alcohol A", "Acid A", etc. Your instructor will assign the appropriate acid/alcohol combination for you to use. Using the table on the next page,

add the appropriate amounts of the respective acid and alcohol into the Erlenmeyer flask. Quantities of liquids are expressed in volume (ml) and solids are indicated in mass (grams). You will use these masses and/or volumes to support your conclusion so it is important that they be recorded as accurately as possible. It is advisable to try and get reasonably close (to within about 0.2 grams or 0.2 ml) of the quantity specified and record the actual amount you use accurately on the data page. Using too much of either the acid or the alcohol could (but not in all cases) create a problem because the odor of the stoichiometrically excess reagent could possibly "hide" the odor of the ester you are trying to make. You will find graduated cylinders labeled with the identity of each of the different acids and alcohols. Use only those for the acid and/or alcohol assigned to you. Mixing the different acids and alcohols in a common graduated cylinder could cause a mixture of esters to be produced and complicate your ability to identify the ester assigned to you.

ESTER	ACID	ALCOHOL
1	8.0 ml Acid E	10.0 ml Alcohol B
2	2.5 grams Acid A	10.0 ml Alcohol F
3	2.5 grams Acid A	10.0 ml Alcohol A
4	9.5 ml Acid B	10.0 ml Alcohol A
5	9.5 ml Acid B	18.5 ml Alcohol C
6	5.0 ml Acid B	14.0 ml Alcohol D
7	6.0 ml Acid B	7.9 ml Alcohol E
8	2.5 grams Acid C	6.3 ml Alcohol F
9	2.5 grams Acid D	6.3 ml Alcohol F

4. Using a graduated cylinder, **CAREFULLY** add about 2 ml of concentrated H_2SO_4 to the mixture. **CAUTION:** Concentrated H_2SO_4 can cause burns: make sure you use gloves when handling it. This is the acid catalyst needed to speed up the reaction. Add the magnetic stir bar to the flask.

5. Since water is a product of the reaction and can reduce the amount of ester according to LeChatelier's principle, we also add a desiccant to help remove the water as it is formed. In the hood is a bottle of DRIERITE: this will help "suck up" the water as it is formed. Add about 10-15 crystals to the reaction mixture.

50

6. Assemble the apparatus as shown in Figure 5.1. **NOTE: The power cord for the hot plate should run UNDER the hood sash, NOT THROUGH A SLIDING GLASS PANEL. If you have to close (or open) the hood sash quickly you do not want the cord to get tangled and cause the hot plate to flip.** Place the Erlenmeyer flask on a hot plate, start the stirrer, and heat until the mixture is gently boiling. A heater setting of about 4 will be adequate for most hot plates. If the mixture does not actually boil but is very hot, that will be sufficient. Remember, the principal objective of this experiment is to show how such a synthesis can be carried out: optimization of the conditions to obtain the maximum amount of product is a different matter beyond the scope of this exercise. The stirring should be rapid enough so that the mixture remains stirred during the reaction. As the mixture boils, its vapor will reach the cold finger condenser and return to the liquid state, dripping back into the Erlenmeyer flask: this is called refluxing the reaction mixture. If the liquid volume in the flask decreases during this stage, it can be replenished adding additional acid and alcohol, in the same ratio you previously used, to the mixture. It will be necessary to replenish the ice in the cold finger condenser during the reaction because the heat from the boiling mixture will cause the ice to melt. DO NOT LEAVE THE REACTION MIXTURE UNATTENDED DURING THE REFLUXING STAGE OF THE EXPERIMENT. The second cold finger condenser will be useful to replace the first one so that it can be refilled with ice. NOTE: If the Drierite seems to change color during the reaction it is because it is absorbing large amounts of moisture. If this happens, add some more crystals to the reaction mixture.

FIGURE 5.1 - EXPERIMENTAL APPARATUS

Ice is placed _inside_ the test tube

Cold Finger Condenser made from a Test Tube

Tape, as needed, is applied to the _outside_ of the test tube here

Erlenmeyer Flask

Hot Plate and Stirrer

51

7. Different esters will form at different rates but none of these esters take longer than about 45 minutes . . . and some of them will form very quickly. **CAUTION:** To test for the odor of the ester you should **<u>NEVER</u>** place your nose directly into the opening of the Erlenmeyer flask. There may be hot vapors coming from the reaction mixture, and they could irritate your nasal passages. The safe method of checking for the odor is to remove the cold finger condenser and gently pass it in front of your nose. The odor of the ester will remain on the outer surface of the condenser for at least several minutes. This way, each time you change the cold finger condenser tube you can also check for the presence of the ester aroma.

8. When you have been able to identify the ester you made, turn off the heat and allow the mixture to cool. After the flask has cooled to the point where you can pick it up, you might want to immerse it in an ice/water bath to help cool it more quickly.

9. Dispose of your reaction mixture into the container designated for spent solutions. Then clean and return all equipment to the front bench at the end of your experiment. Return the magnetic stir bar to your instructor to get your I.D. card.

52

LABORATORY REPORT

Your laboratory report <u>must</u> consist of the following sections, worth the indicated point values:

Procedure (submitted before lab)	5 points
Cover Page	5 points
Introduction	15 points
Observations	30 points
Conclusions/Discussion	30 points
Signed Data Page	15 points

A. The Introduction section must include a brief discussion of the process of esterification and the background chemistry related to the synthesis you were assigned. It is effectively your understanding (but not a direct copy) of the concepts presented in the Background section of this manual.

B. Observations are primarily what you saw happening during the reaction.

C. Conclusions/Discussions must reflect back to your experimental results. From the odor you noticed, identify the ester you made, then identify the acid and alcohol used to make it. You should provide explanations for your results here.

THE PROCEDURE MUST BE SUBMITTED BEFORE YOU DO THE EXPERIMENT. FAILURE TO SUBMIT IT ON TIME WILL GIVE NO POINTS FOR THIS SECTION.

NOTE: Your signed data page must be included with your lab report.

DATA PAGE

Code Letter of Acid Used   _____

Mass of Acid Used   _____

Code Letter of Alcohol Used   _____

Mass of Alcohol Used   _____

Odor of Ester Product Formed

Name of Ester (see Table 5.1 on page 48)

INSTRUCTOR'S SIGNATURE_____   DATE_____

EXPERIMENT #6 - KINETICS OF ALCOHOL OXIDATION

OBJECTIVE

This experiment demonstrates a quantitative method of monitoring the rate of alcohol oxidation. Specifically, the order of reaction and kinetic rate constant will be evaluated. Concentration will be monitored spectrophotometrically by applying Beer's Law once the region of maximum absorbance has been determined. Data will be collected using a computer-assisted method incorporating the Vernier LoggerPro System. This will permit more accurate, and more frequent, collection of data than would be possible under normal conditions.

BACKGROUND

Chemical kinetics deals with the study of reaction rates. Some reactions occur very rapidly, like the combustion of gasoline in a car engine. Other reactions take place more slowly, such as the rusting of iron. Simply describing reactions as "fast" or "slow" is inadequate when trying to assess how rapidly a reaction may be expected to take place. A chemical engineer who reports to his boss that a production reaction takes place "pretty fast" is not of much value to his company. In chemical kinetics, describing the rate of a reaction occurs by evaluating the reaction order and kinetic rate constant. Consider the general reaction in solution

$$aA + bB \leftrightarrows Product(s)$$

The kinetic rate expression for such a reaction is generally fit to the expression:

$$rate = k [A]^x [B]^y$$

where [A] and [B] are the concentrations (in mol/L) of A and B in the solution, x is the order of the reaction with respect to A, y is the order of the reaction with respect to B, and k is the kinetic rate constant. The values for x and y do not have any correlation to the stoichiometric coefficients in the balanced equation (a and b), even though in some instances they turn out to be the same. In fact, they can assume virtually any value at all: positive, negative, integer, or fractional. The most common values are 1 or 2 but any others are possible. The value of x or y is called the partial order

and their sum is the overall order of the reaction. The rate can be defined as being how quickly either reactant (A or B) disappears or how quickly the product(s) appear(s). In this experiment, we are going to monitor the rate of disappearance of one of the two reactants.

When more than one reactant is involved, determining the reaction order with respect to each component can be difficult because each reactant is contributing its own impact on the reaction. When this happens, it is easier to determine the reaction order of each component one at a time to reduce the mathematical complexity. This is accomplished by making several runs in which the concentration of all but one reactant is present in an overwhelming excess so that its concentration remains effectively constant during the reaction. This is called a pseudo-order treatment.

The order can be readily determined from a graphical method of analysis if its value is an integer. Table 6.1 indicates the appropriate graph to construct for each of the "common" orders and how the kinetic rate constant can be determined from the data. This is also shown in Figures 13.5 and 13.6 on pages 620 and 621 of your course textbook Chemistry: The Molecular Science, Third Edition by John W. Moore, Conrad L. Stanitski, and Peter C. Jurs.

TABLE 6.1 - GRAPHICAL DETERMINATION OF REACTION ORDER

REACTION ORDER	Y-AXIS	X-AXIS	KINETIC RATE CONSTANT
Zero	$[Cr_2O_7^{-2}]$	Time	-(Slope)
First	$Ln\ [Cr_2O_7^{-2}]$	Time	-(Slope)
Second	$1/[Cr_2O_7^{-2}]$	Time	(Slope)

The experiment we are going to do is one that, hopefully, none of you are familiar with from personal experience. It involves the oxidation of an alcohol, which is the basis for the Breathalyzer test that used to be administered by police officers throughout the country. In most states, a different method involving infrared spectroscopy is now the preferred method of assessing intoxication. In the older Breathalyzer test, alcohols are oxidized to their corresponding aldehydes, carboxylic acids, and/or ketones depending on the nature of the alcohol. A suitable oxidizing agent to carry out this reaction is potassium dichromate ($K_2Cr_2O_7$), which has an intense red-orange color even at low concentrations. When the oxidation is accomplished, the red-orange colored $K_2Cr_2O_7$ is converted to

the very light green colored Cr^{+3} ion, so the reaction can be monitored by keeping track of the color change as the oxidation proceeds. The equation for the reaction is:

$$3 \ C_2H_5OH \ + \ Cr_2O_7^{-2} \ + \ 8 \ H^+ \quad \rightarrow \quad 3 \ CH_3CHO \ + \ 2 \ Cr^{+3} \ + \ 7 \ H_2O$$

The H$^+$ is not involved in the kinetic rate expression for this reaction (the reaction is zero order in H$^+$). The rate expression for this reaction can therefore be written as:

$$rate \ = \ k \ [C_2H_5OH]^x \ [Cr_2O_7^{-2}]^y$$

Because we are going to use a large excess of the alcohol, its concentration during the reaction remains essentially constant and can therefore be removed from the rate expression, becoming a pseudo-order treatment. This new, pseudo-order rate expression is therefore

$$rate \ = \ k' \ [Cr_2O_7^{-2}]^y$$

where k' is called the pseudo-order rate constant and is equal to k $[C_2H_5OH]^x$. The value of x for this reaction is 1. The rate constant we are going to obtain will be k', not k, so we can determine k from the expression

$$k \ = \ \frac{k'}{[C_2H_5OH]}$$

The Breathalyzer instrument is fairly expensive and it would not be cost-effective, practical, or feasible to equip every patrol car with one but it is portable enough that it can be readily transported to any scene where it may be needed. Instead, the officers on patrol use a screening device based on the same chemistry, and if the screening device suggests intoxication, the suspect is then taken to the police station for a more accurate determination. This screening device is a glass ampoule that is fitted with a plug of silica gel impregnated with $K_2Cr_2O_7$ and a sulfuric acid catalyst to help speed up the reaction. The suspect blows through a mouthpiece and into the glass ampoule. If the color of the $K_2Cr_2O_7$ plug changes from red-orange to green, it suggests that the level of alcohol in the breath may be high enough to warrant arrest for driving under the influence (DUI) or driving while intoxicated (DWI). This screening device is such a cost effective indicator that it can now be readily found at the checkout counters of auto parts stores like Pep Boys and even in retail department stores like Wal Mart.

The more precise Breathalyzer used at the police station is based on the change in the amount of light of a specific wavelength that is absorbed. This is the basis for the experiment we are going to

do. Because the $Cr_2O_7^{-2}$ ion produced when $K_2Cr_2O_7$ is dissolved in water has a perceptible color, it will strongly absorb visible light of a selected wavelength. The amount of light absorbed is directly proportional to $[Cr_2O_7^{-2}]$. In our experiment the amount of light absorbed will be measured with an instrument called a colorimeter. There are two scales that report the amount of light that is affected by the absorbing molecule: percent transmittance and absorbance. We are going to use the absorbance (A), which is proportional to the amount of light absorbed according to Beer's Law:

$$A = \varepsilon\, b\, c$$

where A is the measured absorbance, ε is a constant of proportionality called the molar absorptivity, b is the path length or the thickness of the solution that the light passes through, and c is the concentration of the absorbing molecule. In this experiment we are going to keep b constant at exactly 1.00 cm so that the expression reduces to

$$A = \varepsilon\, c$$

By constructing a plot showing $[Cr_2O_7^{-2}]$ on the x-axis against Absorbance on the y-axis we can determine the molar absorptivity, ε, which is the slope of the best straight line through the points. The software we use to collect our data will give us both absorbance and percent transmittance (%T). Each of the %T values we observe will have been converted into absorbance using the relation:

$$A = 2 - \log (\%T)$$

First we need to know the wavelength where $Cr_2O_7^{-2}$ absorbs the strongest because this is where the light beam will be most sensitive to changes in concentration. The colorimeter we are using has four wavelengths available: 430 nm, 470 nm, 565 nm and 635 nm. We scan these four wavelengths to see where the absorbance is the maximum, and we then use that wavelength for the rest of the experiment.

This experiment is divided into three parts. In Part A we determine the wavelength where the $Cr_2O_7^{-2}$ absorbance is strongest. In Part B we construct a Beer's Law calibration curve to determine the quantitative correlation between absorbance and $[Cr_2O_7^{-2}]$. In Part C we conduct the actual kinetics study by measuring the absorbance of the reacting system as a function of time. Once the data are collected, absorbance is converted to $[Cr_2O_7^{-2}]$ using the value of ε found in Part B, then the appropriate graphs are constructed to determine the reaction order and rate constant.

58

EXPERIMENTAL PROCEDURE

CAUTION: THE $K_2Cr_2O_7$ SOLUTIONS USED IN THIS EXPERIMENT ALSO CONTAIN H_2SO_4 (SULFURIC ACID) CATALYST. THIS SOLUTION CAN CAUSE SKIN BURNS. USE DISPOSABLE GLOVES AND EXERCISE CARE WHEN HANDLING THESE SOLUTIONS. IF YOU SHOULD SPILL ANY OF THE SOLUTION ON YOU WASH THE AFFECTED AREA WITH PLENTY OF WATER.

NOTE: THE SOLUTIONS USED IN THIS EXPERIMENT CONTAIN CHROMIUM, WHICH CANNOT BE POURED DOWN THE DRAIN. A WASTE BOTTLE WILL BE AVAILABLE FOR DISPOSAL OF ALL WASTE SOLUTIONS CONTAINING CHROMIUM.

A. DETERMINING THE WAVELENGTH OF MAXIMUM ABSORBANCE

1. The laptop computer in the lab will be connected to the LoggerPro interface and a Vernier colorimeter, which is where all of the spectral measurements will be made. In Parts B and C, the data will be collected automatically by the computer and stored in a data file, which you can then email to yourself before you leave the lab today. In Part A we are only interested in "where" to work for the rest of the experiment, and these data will not be used in any calculations, so we are going to manually record that data on page 66.

2. Open the LoggerPro 3.1 program by double clicking on the **CHEM 102 - Beer's Law** icon on the desktop. You will see a spreadsheet with three columns (concentration, %T, and absorbance) plus a graph that will plot your data. The x-axis of the graph will go from zero to 0.005M, and the y-axis will go from zero to 1.0 absorbance unit.

3. Fill a sample cell about 3/4 with distilled water, then place the plastic cap on it and place it into the sample compartment of the colorimeter. You will notice that two of the sides of the sample cell are ridged and the other two are clear. One of the two clear sides should face the arrow in the back of the colorimeter sample compartment. Before placing the cell in the sample compartment, wipe it with a Kimwipe or other soft tissue. This removes fingerprints, which could affect the light and give an inaccurate reading. Set the wavelength to 430 nm using the **<** button. Press the **CAL** button and a red light will flash for a few moments. When the light stops flashing, it is calibrated. Replace the cell containing water with another one containing the stock solution of $K_2Cr_2O_7$ that is about 0.004M. You will find this solution stored in a plastic squeeze

bottle either on the front bench or in the fume hood. Don't forget to wipe off the surface of the sample cell before you place it in the colorimeter. Close the sample compartment cover, and record the absorbance on your data page when it has stabilized.

4. Change the wavelength to 470 nm using the **>** button, then repeat Step #3 at this new wavelength. Every time you change the wavelength, the calibration with water must be repeated because the water itself will absorb some of the light.

5. Repeat this until you have measured the absorbance at each of the four wavelengths. If you notice one (or more) reading(s) that give a slightly negative absorbance, it is OK. This means that the value is essentially zero, within the limits of the instrument uncertainty. It only means that you are at a part of the spectrum that shows virtually no absorbance at all.

B. BEER'S LAW

NOTE: THROUGHOUT THE REST OF THIS EXPERIMENT USE ONLY THE SAME TWO SAMPLE CELLS. ONE IS FOR THE WATER BLANK AND THE OTHER IS FOR THE SAMPLE(S). REMEMBER THAT PATH LENGTH AFFECTS THE ABSORBANCE, SO IF YOU ALWAYS USE THE SAME CELL FOR ALL SAMPLES, THERE IS NO UNCERTAINTY ARISING FROM SLIGHT DIFFERENCES IN PATH LENGTH FROM DIFFERENT CELLS.

1. Examine your tabulated data from Part A and find the wavelength where the absorbance was the greatest. This will be the "working wavelength" for the rest of the experiment. Set the wavelength to this value and calibrate the instrument with water, as you did in Step #3 of Part A. No further adjustments to any control will be necessary for the rest of the experiment.

2. Remove the cell with water and place the cell containing the stock solution of approximately 0.0040M $K_2Cr_2O_7$ into the sample compartment. As before, make sure the clear side of the cell faces the arrow inside the colorimeter. Click on **COLLECT** at the top of the chart. When the absorbance reading has stabilized, click **KEEP** and then manually enter the exact concentration stated on the bottle of the $K_2Cr_2O_7$ solution. Press **ENTER** to store the data.

3. On the front bench you will find some plastic squeeze bottles with solutions of $K_2Cr_2O_7$ of varying concentrations. To test the adherence of $K_2Cr_2O_7$ to Beer's Law we need to determine the

correlation between the absorbance and concentration for each of these solutions. Empty the contents of the sample cell into a small beaker you can use to store solutions designated for disposal at the end of the experiment. Rinse the cell a few times with distilled water. Using the same cell you used above (to make sure the path length remains constant), place enough of the next solution to fill the cell about 3/4. Repeat Step #2 for each dilution of $K_2Cr_2O_7$ solution supplied. As you enter the data, you will notice that the points are plotted on the graph so you can get a visual indication of just how well the solution adheres to Beer's Law (i.e., the data appear as a straight line). Add all of the solutions for disposal to the beaker.

4. When you have measured the absorbance for each of the four concentrations, place the cell containing water back in the colorimeter and record its absorbance (entering 0.00M for the concentration). This is a valid data point since there should be no absorbance when the concentration is zero.

5. Look at the graph to determine if the data are usable. According to Beer's Law, there should be a linear relation between absorbance and concentration. Does your graph show this? If so, then you are ready to move on to Part C, but first we have to save these data. First, click on **STOP** to end the data collection. Next, go up to the **FILE** menu and select **EXPORT AS TEXT**. You will want to save your data to the **DESKTOP**. Give the file a name that you will be able to recognize later when you are doing your report: since this was a Beer's Law study, why not use Beer's Law as the file name? When you have saved the data, go to the **FILE** menu and select **EXIT**. You will be asked if you want to save changes made to **CHEM 102 - Beer's Law.** Select **NO** so it will be all set up for the next class. All of your data have already been saved in its own file.

6. If your data from Part B are not acceptable, then the study must be repeated. Go to the **DATA** menu and select **CLEAR ALL DATA**. This will remove all old data from the display, at which point you will be ready to repeat Part B.

C. KINETIC STUDY OF ALCOHOL OXIDATION

1. Open the LoggerPro 3.1 program by double clicking on the **CHEM 102 - Kinetics Run** icon on the desktop. You will see a spreadsheet with three columns (time in seconds, %T, and absorbance) plus a graph that will plot your data. The x-axis of the graph will go from zero to 1200 seconds (20 minutes), and the y-axis will go from zero to 0.6-absorbance unit.

61

2. Into the same sample cell you used for the different solutions of $K_2Cr_2O_7$ in Part B, dispense the stock $K_2Cr_2O_7$ solution that is approximately 0.004M. The solution for this part of the experiment is stored in a container that will dispense exactly 1.50 ml when one full plunger of liquid is used. There are two different types of dispensing pipets in the lab. For one type, lift the plunger until it stops (DO NOT RESET THE VOLUME SETTINGS USING THE ADJUSTMENT SCREW), then place the sample cell under the dispensing tip and depress the plunger. Into the same sample cell, and using the same procedure dispense 1.50 ml of the stock ethanol (C_2H_5OH) solution that is approximately 0.60M, which also can be found in a dispensing container. For the other type of dispensing pipet just depress the plunger. At exactly the same time the solutions are mixed, start the data collection process be clicking on **COLLECT** at the top of the chart. Place the cap on the sample cell, invert it a few times to insure that the solution is well mixed, and then place it in the colorimeter sample compartment after wiping the outside surface with a Kimwipe. Again, make sure the clear side of the cell faces the arrow inside the colorimeter. The program is set to collect data every 30 seconds, so you will have a maximum of 30 seconds to mix the contents and place it in the sample compartment. NOTE: If you do not mix the solution well before placing it in the colorimeter, there may be concentration gradients that can cause data with a lot of "scatter" to it. Also, it could cause the data to "fall out to zero" at the end of the run. Record the exact concentration of the ethanol solution on the data page.

3. You will notice that the absorbance readings will not be steady: they will continue to decrease with time because the reaction will be taking place, reducing [$K_2Cr_2O_7$]. Every 30 seconds, the LoggerPro system will record the absorbance and display it both in the spreadsheet and on the graph. The program is set up to accumulate data for as long as 20 minutes but you may be able to stop the run earlier than that. The absorbance will steadily decline during the reaction and then eventually either reach zero or stabilize at some finite value. If you notice that the absorbance seems to be constant for several data points, the reaction is complete (or has attained chemical equilibrium) and the experiment can be stopped even if it has run less than 20 minutes. The rate of a chemical reaction increases as temperature increases. If the room is warm, the reaction will proceed faster than it will in a cold room so you probably would not have to let the experiment run for the entire 20 minutes. It is important to collect some data when the reaction is nearing

completion and the absorbance is not changing very fast with time. This is critical when trying to determine the reaction order because if you do not allow the reaction to proceed long enough, several different graphical plots will appear to give "good" straight lines and deciding on the correct order can be very difficult. It is much better to let it run a few minutes longer now than to be faced with much more time later in trying to complete the calculations. If you decide to end the run before the entire 20 minutes has passed, click on **STOP** to end the data collection. If you let the experiment run for the entire 20 minutes, then **STOP** will be automatically selected at the end of the run.

4. Look at the graph to determine if the data are usable. Unlike Part B, there should not necessarily be a linear relation between absorbance and concentration but there should be some type of "trend" to the data. Does your graph show this? If so, then you are ready to save these data. To do this, go up to the **FILE** menu and select **EXPORT AS TEXT**. You will want to save your data to the **DESKTOP**. Give the file a name that you will be able to recognize later when you are doing your report: since this was a Kinetics study, why not use that in the file name? When you have saved the necessary data, go to the **FILE** menu and select **EXIT**. You will be asked if you want to save the any of the changes made to **CHEM 102 - Kinetics Run.** Select **NO** so it will be all set up for the next class. All of your data have already been saved in its own file.

5. If your data from Part C are not acceptable, then the study must be repeated. Go to the **DATA** menu and select **CLEAR ALL DATA**. This will remove all old data from the display, at which point you will be ready to repeat Part C with a new set of solutions.

6. At the end of your experiment empty the sample cells into the beaker with the solution designated for disposal, clean up your work area and return the sample cells to the front bench. Empty the beaker with the used solutions into the container marked for disposal.

7. When you return to the desktop, you will see your data files there, identified by the names you assigned. You will need these files to complete your lab report. You can email them to yourself from the PC, which is equipped with a wireless Internet card. Because there can sometimes be problems with the connectivity, it is probably a good idea to bring along a USB Flash Drive to store your data. CAUTION: The computer is already set up for the appropriate wireless connection network. If you try to change to a different one, chances are very good that it will not work properly. DO NOT CHANGE THE WIRELESS NETWORK SETTING.

63

8. After you have transferred your data files, move them to the recycle bin to delete them from the system. Your instructor will not sign your data sheet until all of these steps have been completed.

TREATMENT OF THE DATA

1. Open your Beer's Law data file using an application that can be used to graph the data, such as Microsoft Excel.

2. Using the data from Part B, prepare a Beer's Law calibration curve by plotting absorbance on the y-axis and concentration on the x-axis. By the method of linear regression using all of the data, determine the slope of the best straight line: this is ε, which you will need to determine $[K_2Cr_2O_7]$ in Part C. According to Beer's Law, $[K_2Cr_2O_7]$ can be determined from the absorbance:

$$[K_2Cr_2O_7] = \frac{Absorbance}{\varepsilon}$$

3. Open your Kinetic study data file using an application that can be used to graph the data, such as Excel. Before doing any calculations, scan the data, paying particular attention to the points at the end of the run. This experiment is designed to evaluate kinetics, which means that the reaction must be taking place and it must not have reached equilibrium. If the last few data points show the SAME value for absorbance, the reaction has reached equilibrium (the reaction appears to have stopped because the rates of the forward and reverse reactions are the same) and they must not be included. If there are some number of the SAME absorbance values, keep the first one and delete the others. This is not "tampering" with the data. The scope of the experiment does not include equilibrium, and deleting the repeated values removes that aspect of the data, leaving only the kinetic portion.

4. Using your value of ε from Part B, convert each absorbance into $[K_2Cr_2O_7]$.

5. To determine the reaction order, it is necessary to plot each curve described in Table 6.1. The correct order will be determined by the graph that gives the best straight line. You can determine the best straight line from linear regression. Just how well the data fits the straight-line relation is evaluated by using a statistical quantity known as the correlation coefficient, r. The closer r is to +1 (for a positive slope) or -1 (for a negative slope), the better the straight line. Base your determination of reaction order on the best straight line from the r-value. When using Microsoft

64

Excel, along with the trend line (the result of regression analysis) you can also retrieve a value listed as R^2. This is called the variance and it is the square of the correlation coefficient: just take the square root of this value and you will have the correlation coefficient. If you use the **REGRESSION** selection under **DATA ANALYSIS** under the **TOOLS** menu, you will see much more statistical information than is needed here. In this output, Excel labels it as "Multiple R" instead of correlation coefficient. The pseudo-order kinetic rate constant, k', will be determined from the slope as described in Table 6.1. Determine the "true" rate constant by dividing the pseudo-order constant by the starting concentration of C_2H_5OH. When doing this calculation, keep in mind that the C_2H_5OH was diluted with an equal volume of $K_2Cr_2O_7$, so the actual starting concentration in the reaction mixture is one-half the concentration of the stock solution.

LABORATORY REPORT

Your laboratory report <u>must</u> consist of the following sections, worth the indicated point values:

Procedure (submitted before lab)	5 points
Cover Page	5 points
Introduction	15 points
Experimental Data and Graphs	50 points
Conclusions/Discussion	10 points
Signed Data Page	15 points

A. The Introduction section must include a brief discussion of the principles of kinetics and your understanding of what the experiment is designed to demonstrate. Briefly discuss the graphs that will be constructed from the experimental data. It is effectively your understanding (but not a direct copy) of the concepts presented in the Background section of this manual.

B. The Experimental Data and Graphs section must contain all of the calculations listed in the TREATMENT OF THE DATA section. Also, it is to contain a printout of all of your raw data and the following four graphs:

1. Beer's Law calibration curve from data in Part B

2. Plot of $[K_2Cr_2O_7]$ vs. time to determine if the reaction is zero order (from Part C)

3. Plot of Ln $[K_2Cr_2O_7]$ vs. time to determine if the reaction is 1st order (from Part C)

4. Plot of $1/[K_2Cr_2O_7]$ vs. time to determine if the reaction is 2nd order (from Part C)

C. Conclusions/Discussions must reflect back to your data and experimental results. You should provide explanations for your results here.

THE PROCEDURE MUST BE SUBMITTED BEFORE YOU DO THE EXPERIMENT. FAILURE TO SUBMIT IT ON TIME WILL GIVE NO POINTS FOR THIS SECTION.

NOTE: Your signed data page must be included with your lab report.

66

DATA PAGE

NAME_____ SECTION_____ DATE_____

PART A - DETERMINING THE WAVELENGTH OF MAXIMUM ABSORBANCE

WAVELENGTH (nm)	ABSORBANCE
430	_____
470	_____
565	_____
635	_____

PART C - KINETIC STUDY OF ALCOHOL OXIDATION

Concentration of Stock Ethanol Solution   _____ M

INSTRUCTOR'S SIGNATURE_____ DATE_____

EXPERIMENT #7 - ACIDS AND BASES

OBJECTIVE

The primary objective of this experiment is to recognize the differences between acids and bases, how they react with each other to achieve neutralization, and how to determine the acid content of a household material. By the technique of titration, the amount of acid or base can be quickly and accurately obtained. The endpoint of a titration will be monitored using both an indicator and a pH meter.

BACKGROUND

1. ACIDS, BASES, AND TITRATION

Many different theories of acids and bases have been proposed but the one most often used is the Bronsted-Lowry theory, in which an acid is defined as being a proton (H^+ ion) donor while a base is a proton acceptor. When either an acid or a base is dissolved in water, a conjugate acid and conjugate base form as products of the reaction. The conjugate acid is the initial base plus the proton it accepted from the acid. The conjugate base is that which was initially the acid minus its proton. As an example, consider HCl, a common strong acid:

$$HCl \quad + \quad H_2O \quad \rightarrow \quad H_3O^+ \quad + \quad Cl^-$$

When the HCl molecule dissolves in water it donates a proton (H^+) to the H_2O molecule, causing it to become H_3O^+. HCl is therefore the acid because it has donated a proton. The H_2O molecule, on the other hand, has accepted the proton, so it is the base. Looking at the products of the reaction, we find H_3O^+ formed from the base (H_2O) plus a donated proton, so it is therefore the conjugate acid. Similarly, the Cl^- ion formed from the acid (HCl) minus its proton, so it is the conjugate base.

Another definition of acids and bases, by the Arrhenius theory, states acids give H^+ (or H_3O^+) in water while bases give OH^- in water. Since acids and bases are in a sense opposite, it is reasonable to expect that they could "cancel" or neutralize each other if mixed in the proper stoichiometric ratio. This is the basis for acid-base neutralization reactions. Consider the reaction between the strong acid HCl and the strong base NaOH:

68

$$HCl \quad + \quad NaOH \quad \rightarrow \quad NaCl \quad + \quad H_2O$$

When dissolved in water, HCl dissociates into H^+ and Cl^- ions while the NaOH will dissociate into Na^+ and OH^- ions. In this neutralization reaction, the H^+ from the acid chemically unites with the OH^- from the base to form water (one product of all acid-base neutralization reactions), and the remaining two ions form NaCl. To determine the amount of acid present in an unknown, we merely add a known base to the acid until we have neutralized the solution with the stoichiometric amount of base. This is the guiding principle for a titration. In order to determine when the neutralization is complete we can use indicators that change color when correct amounts have been added. The color change is due to structural changes in the indicator molecule that are caused by the acidic or basic environment. Different indicators change colors at different levels of acidity. For many acid-base titrations phenolphthalein indicator works very well because it is colorless in acid and a light reddish-pink color when a very slight excess of base is present in a solution.

A titration is accomplished by starting with an unknown acid or base solution. In this experiment, the unknown will be an acid (vinegar). A few drops of phenolphthalein indicator are added to the acid solution so that a color change will be noticed when the reaction is complete. A base solution of known concentration is then slowly and carefully added to the unknown acid. The amount of base solution added is measured from a calibrated delivery tube called a buret. This is a long tube that is fitted with a stopcock on one end and is open at the other end to allow for filling. The tube is calibrated to indicate the volume of liquid delivered in ml. The base solution is continually added until the reaction is complete. Initially you will not notice any change in the color of the solution, but as the endpoint (the visual point where the reaction is done) is approached, you will notice that a reddish-pink color forms at the point where NaOH contacts the solution in the flask. With agitation, this color will fade, but when the endpoint is reached, the color will persist for at least 30 seconds. As you near the endpoint, the base solution should be added one drop at a time. The objective is to have the color change at the endpoint be as faint as possible. When this is accomplished, the final volume is recorded from the buret. To determine the moles of base used, the concentration of the base solution must be known. From the volume used and concentration of the solution, the number of moles can be determined:

$$moles = (Molarity)(Volume \; in \; Liters)$$

69

Determining what indicator to use can be a little tricky because we need to have some knowledge about the acid(s) or base(s) in the unknown. If a strong acid is titrated with a strong base, the pH at the equivalence point will be exactly 7.00, but if either the acid(s) or base(s) is/are weak, the pH will not be at 7.00 because at least one ion will hydrolyze (react with water) to give a slightly acidic or basic solution at the equivalence point, or the point when stoichiometrically equivalent amounts of acid and base have been added. How far away from a pH of 7.00 the equivalence point is depends on the strength of the weak acid or base. If there is no indication of the pH at the equivalence point, constructing a titration curve is the preferred method of analysis because it replaces the indicator with a pH meter that will function in solutions of any equivalence point pH.

2. TITRATION CURVES

Another method of conducting a titration is to use a pH meter in place of an indicator. Acid solutions have a pH below 7 and bases have a pH above 7. Let us suppose that we are trying to determine the acid content of an unknown solution. The pH electrode is immersed in the solution and a pH below 7 is noted. As the base is slowly added to the acid, the pH gradually increases as the acid is neutralized. At the equivalence point the pH will change dramatically over to the basic side as a very small amount of excess base is added. By plotting the pH vs. the volume of base added, a graph called a titration curve results. At the equivalence point a steep inflection is noted in the curve.

Let us suppose we place 25.00 ml of 0.100M HCl in a beaker and titrate it with 0.100M NaOH. The pH is recorded after certain NaOH additions, giving the following data:

VOLUME OF NaOH (ml)	pH	VOLUME OF NaOH (ml)	pH
0.00	1.00	25.00	7.00
5.00	1.18	25.05	10.00
10.00	1.37	25.10	10.30
15.00	1.60	25.50	11.00
20.00	1.95	26.00	11.29
24.00	2.69	30.00	11.96
24.50	3.00	35.00	12.22
24.90	3.70	40.00	12.36
24.95	4.00	45.00	12.46

70

A titration curve is a plot of these data with the volume of titrant (in this case, 0.100M NaOH solution) on the x-axis and the pH on the y-axis. The curve for these data is given below.

FIGURE 7.1 - TITRATION CURVE FOR 0.100M HCl WITH 0.100M NaOH

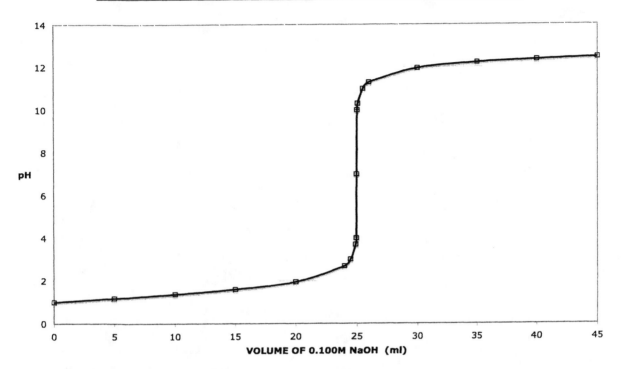

At the equivalence point the pH will change dramatically with only a drop or two of titrant. If a weak acid or base is titrated, the curve will have the same general shape but the inflection will be shifted down or up to reflect the acidic or basic pH at the equivalence point. Examples of typical titration curves are shown in Figures 17.5 (on page 838), Figure 17.6 (on page 840) and Figure 17.8 (on page 843) of your course textbook Chemistry: The Molecular Science, Third Edition by John W. Moore, Conrad L. Stanitski, and Peter C. Jurs.

In a titration curve, the equivalence point occurs where the change in pH (ΔpH) relative to the volume change (ΔV) is the greatest. Mathematically, this is evaluated by considering pairs of successive data points and calculating the quantity [ΔpH/ΔV]. Using the data given in the table above, we find [ΔpH/ΔV] for the 0.00 and 5.00 ml data pairs to be

$$\frac{\Delta pH}{\Delta V} = \frac{1.18 - 1.00}{5.00 \text{ ml} - 0.00 \text{ ml}} = 0.036 \text{ pH units/ml}$$

By comparison, using the data at the equivalence point (the 24.95 and 25.00 ml data pairs) we arrive at

$$\frac{\Delta pH}{\Delta V} = \frac{7.00 - 4.00}{25.00 \text{ ml} - 24.95 \text{ ml}} = 60 \text{ pH units/ml}$$

The rate of change of pH with respect to volume is about 1700 times greater at the equivalence point than it was at the beginning of the titration. When conducting a titration, it is important to use very small increments (only about 1 drop, or approximately 0.05 ml) of titrant when you are near the equivalence point.

A titration curve also gives you insight into what indicator to select. A useful indicator will have a color change in the region of the inflection (the quickest change of pH with respect to volume). Strong acids titrated with strong bases will generally have a wide inflection region, indicating that there is a wide range of pH change for indicators from which to choose. The useful indicator range for the titration curve of Figure 7.1 is shown, and it is indeed quite large. If either the acid or the base is weak, the size of the inflection will decrease, and the useful pH range from which to select an indicator will shrink.

When the acid is weak (such as the acetic acid present in vinegar), the titration curve can also be used to determine the equilibrium constant, K_a, for the equilibrium condition that is established:

$$CH_3COOH + H_2O \rightleftharpoons H_3O^+ + CH_3COO^-$$

The equilibrium constant expression for this system is:

$$K_a = \frac{[H_3O^+][CH_3COO^-]}{[CH_3COOH]}$$

When the reaction is halfway to the equivalence point, half of the CH_3COOH has been converted to CH_3COO^-, which means that $[CH_3COOH] = [CH_3COO^-]$. This reduces the K_a expression to

$$K_a = [H_3O^+]$$

or, more conveniently

$$pK_a = pH$$

NOTE: This expression is only valid halfway to the equivalence point and only for a weak acid. To determine the value of K_a from pK_a, we use the expression:

$$K_a = 10^{-pH}$$

where the pH is understood to be the value _halfway_ to the equivalence point.

72

EXPERIMENTAL PROCEDURE

WARNING: Do not assume that any glassware you obtain from the front bench is clean. Wash all glassware with soap and water, followed by a thorough rinsing with water. Small amounts of acidic or basic impurities from other solutions that have been in the glassware could seriously affect your results, which can make completing your calculations, and ultimately writing your lab report, much more difficult.

NOTE: When doing any titration it is best to start with a full buret of the titrant. This eliminates the need to refill during the analysis. If you have to refill a buret during a titration, remove the beaker or flask containing your sample from beneath the buret because if you accidentally overfill the buret, the spilled solution could drip into your sample, making your analysis worthless.

1. Obtain a "pH pen" from the beaker on the front bench. They are stored in a solution to keep the membrane moist. To calibrate the instrument, set the OFF/ON switch on the top of the meter to "ON". Immerse the electrode into a pH 7.00 buffer solution, then set the pH 7 trim adjustment (the screw to the left of the OFF/ON switch) to give a display of exactly 7.00 pH units. Repeat this step using a pH 4.00 buffer and set the pH 4 trim adjustment (the screw to the right of the OFF/ON switch) to give a display of exactly 4.00 pH units. A small screwdriver or the tip of a spatula can be used to make the trim adjustments.

2. Place about 70 ml of the standardized NaOH solution in a 100 ml beaker. Record the exact concentration of the NaOH solution from the label of the bottle, as you will need this in doing your calculations. Use this solution to fill a buret with standardized NaOH. Open the stopcock to allow some of the solution to fill the tip. Close the stopcock when the volume is near zero ml. Record the exact starting volume to within 0.02 ml. When recording volumes, you will notice that the liquid forms a curved surface, called a meniscus, in the buret. To obtain an accurate reading, you need to read the bottom of the meniscus. You will notice that the buret is graduated in 0.1 ml increments. The second decimal place must be estimated from the position of the meniscus. In your mind, imagine the region between two different 0.1 ml graduation marks divided into ten smaller divisions, and estimate the position of the meniscus in these imaginary divisions. When reading the meniscus, look at it at eye level--do not look above or below the meniscus as this leads to an inaccurate reading.

73

3. Add between 4.0 and 4.2 grams of vinegar to a clean 250 ml beaker. **DO NOT POUR THE VINEGAR INTO A BEAKER FIRST. USE A PLASTIC PIPET TO REMOVE THE VINEGAR DIRECTLY FROM THE BOTTLE.** Using too much could cause you to have to refill the buret during the titration and using too little could make interpolating the titration curve very difficult. The weighing should be done on the balance on the front bench having a capability of weighing to 0.001 grams to give four significant figures in your data.

4. To make sure the electrode membrane remains covered, add enough distilled water to bring the total volume up to about 100 ml. You can estimate this volume because it is not needed in any calculations: it is only used to dilute the solution and cover the electrode membrane.

5. Add 2 or 3 drops of phenolphthalein indicator, the pH pen, and a magnetic stirring bar to the solution in the beaker. Place the beaker on a magnetic stirrer and stir the contents to insure that the sample is well mixed.

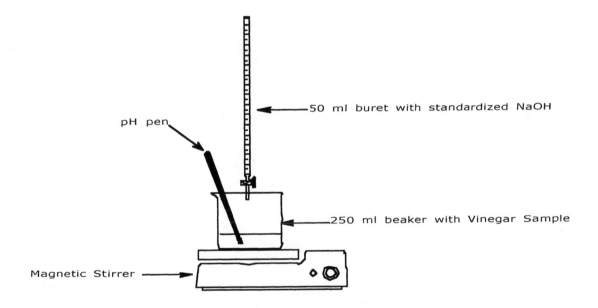

pH pen

50 ml buret with standardized NaOH

250 ml beaker with Vinegar Sample

Magnetic Stirrer

6. Titrate the vinegar by slowly adding about 3 ml of the standardized NaOH solution from the buret while stirring the contents of the beaker. Record the exact volume of NaOH added and the pH of the solution. The solution must be continually stirred, and the pH electrode is left in the solution during the entire titration. If you have a problem recording the pH while the solution is being stirred, turn off the stirrer long enough to record the pH, start it again, then continue the titration.

74

Make accurate notations of both the volume and pH after each addition so that you will be able to construct your titration curve. Continue adding the standardized NaOH solution in approximately 3 ml increments until the pH is near 6. After a pH of about 6, reduce the volume added between pH readings. Remember: Figure 7.1 showed that the pH changes very rapidly at the equivalence point where additions should be only a drop or two. After each addition, record both the total volume of NaOH added and the pH of the solution. You will know that you are near the equivalence point when the faint pink color of the phenolphthalein indicator begins to take longer to fade. In the early stages of the titration, there is a great of excess of acid (relative to the NaOH added) so the color fades almost instantly. As the acid is consumed, the NaOH has a tougher time "finding" unreacted acid so the pink color of the indicator takes longer to fade. When you are near the equivalence point, reduce the volume of NaOH added to just a few drops at a time until the indicator turns color; then again return the increments to about 2 or 3 ml. The data on page 69 (and the graph on page 70) show that the pH will change very quickly at the equivalence point so you want to make sure you go very slowly in this area. Make a notation of the volume when the indicator turns color. You need at least five data points after the indicator turns color.

7. At the end of your experiment, rinse out and return all glassware to the front bench and clean up your work area. Return the magnetic stir bar to your instructor to get back your I.D. card. The magnetic stirrer and buret assembly can be left on the bench for the next group. Return the pH pen to the beaker of water on the front bench to prevent the membrane from drying out. To help conserve the batteries, make sure you turn off power to the pH pen before putting it back.

TREATMENT OF DATA

1. Construct a titration curve from your pH (y-axis) and volume of NaOH (x-axis) data. The volume plotted is the actual volume delivered from the buret. If you did not start with an initial volume of exactly 0.00 ml on the buret, the starting volume will need to be subtracted from each volume recorded. The volume at the steep inflection of the curve is the volume necessary for complete neutralization of the vinegar. Notice how this volume compares with the volume you recorded for the color change of the indicator.

75

2. The chemical reaction between CH_3COOH and NaOH involves 1:1 stoichiometry:

$$NaOH \ + \ CH_3COOH \ \rightarrow \ NaCH_3COO \ + \ H_2O$$

Calculate the moles of NaOH added, which is also the number of moles of CH_3COOH in the vinegar sample:

$$\text{moles } CH_3COOH \ = \ \text{moles NaOH} \ = \ \text{(Volume in liters)(Molarity of NaOH solution)}$$

3. Using the result from #2 and the molar mass of CH_3COOH, determine the mass (in grams) of CH_3COOH in the vinegar sample.

4. Using the result from #3 and the mass of vinegar you used, calculate the % CH_3COOH in the vinegar:

$$\% \ CH_3COOH \ = \ \frac{\text{mass of } CH_3COOH}{\text{mass of vinegar}} \ \times \ 100\%$$

5. Go back to the equivalence point of your titration curve from #1. Calculate half of the volume. For example, if your equivalence point was at exactly 30.00 ml, the half volume would be 15.00 ml. Interpolate the titration curve to determine the pH at the half volume: this is pK_a of the acid. It might be easier to obtain this value from your tabulated data. If you do not have a data point corresponding to exactly half of the equivalence volume, you can interpolate the data. The change in pH with respect to volume is minimal at this point since it is far away from the equivalence point and interpolating the data is an accurate method of determining the pH needed. Calculate K_a of the acid using

$$K_a \ = \ 10^{-(\text{pH at half volume})}$$

Compare your value of K_a with the known value for CH_3COOH, which can be found in Table 16.2 on page 788 of your course textbook Chemistry: The Molecular Science, Third Edition by John W. Moore, Conrad L. Stanitski, and Peter C. Jurs.

LABORATORY REPORT

Your laboratory report <u>must</u> consist of the following sections, worth the indicated point values:

Procedure	5 points
Cover Page	5 points
Introduction	15 points
Experimental Data and Calculations	40 points
Conclusions/Discussion	20 points
Signed Data Page	15 points

A. The Introduction section must include a brief discussion of the differences between acids and bases and a statement regarding the function of indicators. Since a neutralization reaction is studied, a short description/definition of each of the following terms/concepts is also appropriate: neutralization, endpoint, equivalence point, titration, and back titration. It is effectively your understanding (but not a direct copy) of the concepts presented in the Background section of this manual.

B. The Experimental Data and Calculations section is composed of all data recorded on the data sheet as well as the calculations requested in the TREATMENT OF DATA. Calculations should be done in sufficient detail using units to indicate your level of understanding.

C. Conclusions/Discussions must reflect back to your data and experimental results. Indicate whether your data verify or dispute the claim that vinegar is a 5% solution of acetic acid. Support your conclusions with your experimental data. You should provide explanations for your results here.

THE PROCEDURE MUST BE SUBMITTED BEFORE YOU DO THE EXPERIMENT. FAILURE TO SUBMIT IT ON TIME WILL GIVE NO POINTS FOR THIS SECTION.

NOTE: Your signed data page must be included with your lab report.

77

DATA PAGE

Concentration of standardized NaOH Solution _____ M

Mass of Vinegar Used _____ grams

VOLUME OF NaOH	pH	VOLUME OF NaOH	pH
_____	_____	_____	_____
_____	_____	_____	_____
_____	_____	_____	_____
_____	_____	_____	_____
_____	_____	_____	_____
_____	_____	_____	_____
_____	_____	_____	_____
_____	_____	_____	_____
_____	_____	_____	_____
_____	_____	_____	_____
_____	_____	_____	_____
_____	_____	_____	_____
_____	_____	_____	_____
_____	_____	_____	_____
_____	_____	_____	_____
_____	_____	_____	_____
_____	_____	_____	_____
_____	_____	_____	_____
_____	_____	_____	_____

INSTRUCTOR'S SIGNATURE_____ DATE_____

78

EXPERIMENT #8 - ELECTROCHEMICAL CELLS

OBJECTIVE

This experiment demonstrates how to construct a spontaneous electrochemical cell and determine the voltage generated. By measuring the potential under standard state conditions, we can also determine the equilibrium constant for the reaction.

BACKGROUND

We encounter electrochemical cells every day when we use a dry cell battery or the lead-sulfuric acid battery in an automobile. The voltage is generated as a result of a reduction/oxidation, or redox, reaction. Oxidation is a process in which one or more electrons are lost while reduction is a process in which electrons are gained. In any cell, both processes must take place: electrons cannot be gained in one part of the reaction unless they are lost in another part. Consider what happens if a strip of copper foil is immersed in a solution of silver nitrate:

$$2\,Ag^+ \quad + \quad Cu \quad \rightarrow \quad Cu^{+2} \quad + \quad 2\,Ag$$

This reaction occurs spontaneously at room temperature. As the reaction proceeds, electrons are transferred from the copper metal to the silver ion, forming a layer of elemental silver that deposits on the copper foil and appears to "tarnish" the surface. Also, the solution turns blue from the Cu^{+2} ions that are formed. If a voltmeter is used to measure the potential, it would be found to be +0.46 volts when the Ag^+ and Cu^{+2} ions are both at a concentration of 1M and the temperature is 25°C (298K). When the concentrations and the temperature change, the potential will also change. A spontaneous cell such as this will generate a positive potential difference that is specific for each reaction. The lead/sulfuric acid battery used in an automobile generates about 2 volts: six of these are connected in series to generate the 12 volts that we associate with a battery of this type. A dry cell battery such as a "C" or "D" cell generates about 1.5 volts. This type of cell is called galvanic or voltaic.

By consulting a table of standard reduction potentials, designated E°, we can predict which reactions will occur spontaneously. Standard reduction potentials can be thought of as a relative

listing of the tendency for any species to undergo reduction. Since potential values are dependent on concentration and temperature, a set of standard conditions must be specified as a point of reference. The standard conditions for electrochemical cells specify a temperature of 25°C (298K) and 1.00M concentration for all dissolved species. The more positive the value of E°, the more it is likely to undergo reduction. Since any redox reaction must be composed of both a reduction and an oxidation, there must be another half of the reaction that will be the oxidation. The E° values for the reduction of Ag^+ to Ag and the reduction of Cu^{+2} to Cu are as follows:

$$Ag^+ \; + \; e^- \; \rightarrow \; Ag \qquad E° = +0.7994V$$

$$Cu^{+2} \; + \; 2e^- \; \rightarrow \; Cu \qquad E° = +0.337V$$

More comprehensive tables of E° values are given in Table 19.1 on page 939 and also Appendix I on pages A-35 through A-37 of your course textbook Chemistry The Molecular Science, Third Edition by John W. Moore, Conrad L. Stanitski, and Peter C. Jurs. With the two values above we can determine what the spontaneous reaction will be and the voltage corresponding to it. Since the Ag^+ to Ag half reaction is more positive than the Cu^{+2} to Cu reaction, the Ag^+ to Ag reaction is the one that will be the reduction. Consequently, this must mean that the Cu^{+2}/Cu half reaction must occur as an oxidation. This can be expressed by "turning around" the copper half reaction to show two electrons being lost, not gained. If the reaction is reversed, then the sign (but not the magnitude) of E° must also be reversed, from +0.337 volts to -0.337 volts. When these two reactions are written in this fashion we arrive at:

$$Ag^+ \; + \; e^- \; \rightarrow \; Ag \qquad E° = +0.7994V$$

$$Cu \; \rightarrow \; Cu^{+2} \; + \; 2e^- \qquad E° = -0.337V$$

To balance the overall equation properly, we need to balance the number of electrons because the number of electrons lost must be equal to the number of electrons gained. Since the Ag^+/Ag couple involves only one electron and the Cu/Cu^{+2} couple involves two, we need to double the coefficient Ag^+/Ag couple to have two electrons gained. The two equations can now be added together to arrive at the balanced equation, along with its cell potential:

$$Cu \; + \; 2\,Ag^+ \; \rightarrow \; Cu^{+2} \; + \; 2\,Ag \qquad E° = +0.4624V$$

80

Spontaneity of a chemical reaction is determined by the overall E° of the cell. If E° > 0, the reaction is spontaneous and if E° < 0, the reaction will not be spontaneous. For example, if the reaction above is reversed so that the reactants and products are interchanged, E° will be equal to -0.462V, which is a non-spontaneous cell.

It is important to note that doubling the stoichiometric coefficients in an equation does not mean that we double the value of E°: concentration effects on E° are evaluated with the Nernst equation:

$$E_{cell} = E°_{cell} - \frac{RT}{nF} \ln Q \qquad (8-1)$$

In this expression, E_{cell} is the cell potential under non-standard conditions, $E°_{cell}$ is the standard state cell potential, R is the gas law constant, T is the absolute temperature, n is the number of electrons involved, F is the Faraday constant (the charge corresponding to 1 mole of electrons), and Q is called the reaction quotient. Q has the same identical form as the equilibrium constant, K, but the concentrations do not correspond to the equilibrium values. Normally we are only interested in the concentration effects (monitored through the expression for Q) so if we keep the temperature constant at 298K and combine it with the other constants (R and F), and also convert ln Q to log Q (change it from the natural logarithm to the common logarithms), the expression for the Nernst equation becomes

$$E_{cell} = E°_{cell} - \frac{0.0592}{n} \log Q \qquad (8-2)$$

The strength of this expression is the ability to determine the equilibrium constant, K, for an electrochemical reaction from voltage measurements. At equilibrium, the observed cell potential (E_{cell}, but not the standard state cell potential $E°_{cell}$) becomes equal to zero. Substituting E_{cell}=0 into Equation 8-2 and replacing Q with K (since we are now at equilibrium) we can determine the equilibrium constant, K:

$$\log K = \frac{nE°_{cell}}{0.0592} \qquad (8-3)$$

To determine K, we need only the standard state cell potential and the number of electrons involved. For the copper/silver reaction discussed above E° = +0.462 volts and n = 2 electrons:

$$\log K = \frac{(2)(0.4624)}{0.0592} = 15.62$$

which gives K = $10^{15.62}$, or 4.18×10^{15}. Since K >>> 1, we conclude that the reaction proceeds <u>very far to the right</u>, so much so that it is essentially complete.

In this experiment we are going to measure the cell potential corresponding to a variety of different galvanic cells. The experiment will be conducted by connecting isolated regions of different metals in contact with a 1M solution of their respective metal ion: for example Cu metal in contact with Cu^{+2} ion. We shall use a plastic well tray to assemble five different metal/metal ion half-cells, which will then be connected to form assorted galvanic cells. The connection between half-cells will be made using a salt bridge, which will be a thin strip of filter paper moistened with KCl. The salt bridge helps to maintain electrical neutrality during the overall cell reaction.

The overall cell must, by definition, be composed of both an oxidation and a reduction. These processes take place at the two electrodes: the anode is the negative electrode and the site of oxidation, while the cathode is the positive electrode and the site of reduction. In the above copper/silver cell reaction, copper is the anode and silver is the cathode. As the reaction progresses, the mass of the anode will decrease as the copper metal is oxidized to Cu^{+2} while the mass of the cathode will increase as Ag^+ is reduced to Ag metal. When we make measurements of cell potential we must get the polarity correct or the sign of the potential will be reversed. We shall use two different probes, connected to a voltmeter that will complete the circuit. If the recorded potential is positive, we have correctly set up the galvanic (spontaneous) cell. By recording the potential and identifying the metal connected to both the positive and negative electrodes, we shall be able to complete all of the required calculations. If the potential is negative, reverse the probe polarity and record the data.

In this experiment we are going to use the following metal/metal ion combinations. The standard reduction potential for each is indicated for reference.

$$Cu^{+2} + 2e^- \rightarrow Cu \qquad E^\circ = +0.3374V$$

$$Pb^{+2} + 2e^- \rightarrow Pb \qquad E^\circ = -0.126V$$

$$Ni^{+2} + 2e^- \rightarrow Ni \qquad E^\circ = -0.25V$$

$$Zn^{+2} + 2e^- \rightarrow Zn \qquad E^\circ = -0.763V$$

$$Al^{+3} + 3e^- \rightarrow Al \qquad E^\circ = -1.66V$$

82

Using these values we can calculate the theoretical E° for each galvanic cell we are going to construct. From these five different metals, we can arrive at fifteen different combinations of the metals, using two at a time and not repeating any of them. Keep in mind that for a galvanic cell, the reduction reaction (occurring at the cathode, or the positive electrode) will always be the half reaction that is more positive. As part of our calculations, we are going to compare our measured values with the theoretical values. The data will also be used to evaluate the standard reduction potential for four of the five half reactions. Note that the Cu^{+2} to Cu half reaction is the most positive of all the values listed above, meaning that it will always be the reduction reaction. We can use this fact, and the Cu^{+2} to Cu E° value, to evaluate the standard reduction potential for the other five half reactions. For example, let us suppose we measure the potential of a cell reaction involving Zn/Zn^{+2} and Cu^{+2}/Cu and we find that it is 1.102 volts. From these data we can calculate the value of E° for the Zn/Zn^{+2} half reaction. Since the Cu half reaction is the reduction, the Zn half reaction must be the oxidation. We are given the value of E° for the Cu^{+2}/Cu half reaction (+0.337V) and the overall cell potential as measured (+1.102V). Collecting the data in an appropriate table, we arrive at the following:

$$Cu^{+2} + 2e^- \rightarrow Cu \qquad E° = +0.337V$$

$$\underline{Zn \rightarrow Zn^{+2} + 2e^- \qquad\qquad E° = ???????V}$$

$$Cu^{+2} + Zn \rightarrow Cu + Zn^{+2} \qquad E° = +1.102V$$

This gives a value of E° for the Zn to Zn^{+2} half reaction of (1.102V - 0.337V), or +0.765V. The conversion of Zn to Zn^{+2} is an _oxidation_ process, so the standard _reduction_ potential would be the reverse of this, or -0.765V. As you can see, this agrees very favorably with the value of -0.763V in the table.

EXPERIMENTAL PROCEDURE

NOTE: IT IS NOT NECESSARY TO CONSTRUCT TEN DIFFERENT CELLS TO MAKE ALL OF THE MEASUREMENTS LISTED ON THE DATA PAGE. USING THE METHOD LISTED BELOW ONLY REQUIRES ONE PIECE OF EACH METAL AND WILL ALLOW ALL OF THE REQUIRED MEASUREMENTS TO BE MADE.

83

A. CONSTRUCTION OF ELECTROCHEMICAL CELLS

1. Obtain a plastic well tray from the front bench, along with **one** small piece of each of the following metals: Cu, Zn, Al, Pb, and Ni.

2. Place each piece of metal in its own compartment of the well tray. Make sure you keep track of which metal was placed in which compartment. The following arrangement is recommended:

Cu	Zn	Pb
Al	Ni	

3. On the front bench are dropper bottles with salt solutions for each of the metals listed above. Into the appropriate cell of the well tray, place enough of each metal salt solution to cover its respective metal. For example, about 5-10 drops of a solution of Cu^{+2} will adequately cover a small piece of Cu. DO NOT REMOVE THE SOLUTIONS FROM THE FRONT BENCH, AS THE OTHER STUDENTS IN THE CLASS WILL NEED THE SAME SOLUTIONS.

4. Cut a piece of filter paper into thin strips that will be used to connect adjacent cells of the well tray. Do not cut the filter paper strips too large or they will partially cover the metal pieces and could make it difficult to measure the cell potential. A good size for each strip is about 35 mm by 5 mm. Fold the paper over so that it makes contact with each solution in the adjacent cells. For example, if you have Cu/Cu^{+2} next to Zn/Zn^{+2}, fold the paper over so that one end touches the Zn^{+2} solution and the other end touches the Cu^{+2} solution. Place one or two drops of KCl solution on the top of the filter paper to complete the connection between the cells: this forms a salt bridge. Repeat this process until all adjacent cells are connected. All together, there should be seven filter paper connections between adjacent cells.

B. MEASURING CELL POTENTIALS

1. Connect the red test lead to the **"VΩmA"** jack and the black test lead to the **"COM"** jack of the multimeter.

2. Set the **RANGE** switch to the **DC 20V** setting. The display will show a reading of 0.00 volts.

3. Turn to the data sheet on page 86 and locate the first cell to measure, which is Cu and Zn. Place one of the probes on the piece of Cu metal and the other on the Zn metal. The probe must make direct contact with the metal strip that is immersed in a solution of its metal ion. Note the voltage

as displayed on the meter. The display should show a positive value. If it is negative, reverse the polarity and record the new value. Also, record which metal was connected to the red (+) probe and which is connected to the black (-) probe. In some instances (such as with aluminum metal) the initial reading may not be stable. This is because the probe is actually touching some aluminum oxide coated on the surface of the aluminum metal and the oxide coating must be scratched away to make contact with aluminum metal. If this happens, gently scrape the metal surface with the test probe to remove the oxide coating.

4. Repeat Step #3 for each of the combinations listed on the data page.

5. When you have acquired all of your data, dispose of the metals and their corresponding solutions in the waste container on the front bench, and return all equipment to the front bench.

TREATMENT OF THE DATA

1. For each of the electrochemical cells involving Cu, calculate the standard reduction potential for the second metal using your experimental data of the overall cell potential ($E°$) and $E° = +0.337V$ for the Cu^{+2} to Cu reduction. See page 82 for an example of this calculation.

2. For all of the remaining cells, write a balanced equation for the overall cell reaction and compare your experimental value for the overall cell $E°$ to the theoretical values computed using the standard reduction potentials on page 81. Compute the percent error between your experimental value and the theoretical value. When writing the balanced equation, use your data about which metals were the red (+) and black (-) electrodes to help in identifying the oxidation and reduction half reactions.

3. For each of the cells involving copper, calculate the equilibrium constant, K, from your experimental data. List the cells in order of increasing (lowest to highest K) completeness of reaction based on the equilibrium constant.

LABORATORY REPORT

Your laboratory report <u>must</u> consist of the following sections, worth the indicated point values:

Procedure (submitted before lab)	5 points
Cover Page	5 points
Introduction	15 points
Experimental Data and Calculations	45 points
Conclusions/Discussion	15 points
Signed Data Page	15 points

A. The Introduction section must include a brief general discussion of electrochemical cells and the reactions that take place. Indicate the calculations that are to be done based on the experimental data that is collected. It is effectively your understanding (but not a direct copy) of the concepts presented in the Background section of this manual.

B. The Experimental Data and Calculations section is composed of all data recorded on the data page as well as the calculations requested in the TREATMENT OF DATA section. Calculations should be done in sufficient detail to indicate your level of understanding. Because of the number of calculations required, this portion is worth a large percentage of the grade.

C. Conclusions/Discussions must reflect back to your data and experimental results. Comment on any large discrepancies between your experimental values and the theoretical potential. Some of the cells may not match the theoretical values too closely. You should provide explanations for your results here.

THE PROCEDURE MUST BE SUBMITTED BEFORE YOU DO THE EXPERIMENT. FAILURE TO SUBMIT IT ON TIME WILL GIVE NO POINTS FOR THIS SECTION.

NOTE: Your signed data page must be included with your lab report.

DATA PAGE

PART B - MEASURING CELL POTENTIALS

CELL COMPONENTS	(+) PROBE	(-) PROBE	CELL POTENTIAL (VOLTS)
Cu and Zn	_____	_____	_____
Cu and Pb	_____	_____	_____
Cu and Ni	_____	_____	_____
Cu and Al	_____	_____	_____
Zn and Pb	_____	_____	_____
Zn and Ni	_____	_____	_____
Zn and Al	_____	_____	_____
Pb and Ni	_____	_____	_____
Pb and Al	_____	_____	_____
Ni and Al	_____	_____	_____

INSTRUCTOR'S SIGNATURE_____   DATE_____

NOTE: EXPERIMENT #9 ON PAGES 88 THROUGH 100

IS FOR HONORS SECTION LAB CLASSES ONLY.

IF YOU ARE IN ONE OF THE HONORS LAB SECTIONS

(DESIGNATED WITH THE SUFFIX "H" AFTER

YOUR SECTION NUMBER)

YOU WILL BE PERFORMING EXPERIMENT #9

IN PLACE OF EXPERIMENT #5 ON

PREPARATION OF ESTERS

88

EXPERIMENT #9 - SEPARATING MIXTURES BY CHROMATOGRAPHY

OBJECTIVE

This experiment demonstrates two techniques for the separation of mixtures into their components. It involves the use of paper chromatography (PC) for the separation of food dyes and also gas chromatography (GC) for the separation of a mixture of chlorinated hydrocarbons. Unknowns containing one or more of the known components will be examined to determine their composition. For the GC portion of this experiment, data will be collected using a computer-assisted method of data acquisition.

BACKGROUND

Chromatography is a process of separating a mixture into its components based on the use of both a stationary phase and a moving, or mobile, phase. The stationary phase can be a solid that is used by itself or it can be a solid coated with a liquid phase. In the latter case the solid serves merely as a support for the liquid phase. Separation takes place because each of the components of the mixture has a different attraction for the stationary phase and will therefore move along at different rates.

You have probably seen examples of chromatography but don't recognize them. Have you ever printed a report using an inkjet printer and then accidentally gotten a few drops of water on the paper? If you look closely at the printing, you would notice that the black ink seems to "run" and a separation seems to be taking place. It is easier to see the separation if you place a drop of black ink on a moistened paper towel. You would eventually see a starburst pattern of different colors around the perimeter of the drop. The black ink is separated into a rainbow of different colored components through chromatography. The stationary phase is the paper towel or the paper you printed on, and the mobile phase is the water that caused the colors to "run". The separation could be improved if a thin strip of the paper towel was marked with a streak of black ink about an inch from its base and then hung in a glass of water with the bottom of the paper just barely touching the liquid surface. As the water travels up the paper, it carries the ink along with it. The different colors travel at different

rates and after some period of time the strip of paper towel gives a rainbow of colors that all combine to give the black ink you used.

Our PC experiment will focus on food dyes; either alone or as found in a common product like a powdered drink mix. For many years, all food dyes were derived from natural sources, such as the red dye from beets or the green dye from chlorophyll found in spinach leaves. Now almost all dyes used in foods are synthetic, and you may be surprised to find that a food dye you thought was one color is actually a combination of different colors or that different brands of food dyes show different compositions. In fact, all synthetic food dyes and colorings used in the United States by law can be only one or more of the eight federally approved Food, Drug, and Cosmetics (or F,D & C) dyes. Of these eight approved dyes, four of them are very widely used: Yellow #5, Yellow #6, Red #40 and Blue #1. Take a look at labels of products that have artificial coloring and notice how often these four dyes appear. Most other colors are made by combinations of these four. For example, 7 parts of Red #40, 4 parts of Yellow #5, and 1 part of Blue #1 all mixed together gives the color of chocolate. Because the components used in making artificially flavored drinks may be colorless these dyes are often added to beverages to give the desired color (for example, red coloring for a raspberry drink).

In the PC experiment, the stationary phase will be a strip of an absorbent paper and the mobile phase will be water. By carefully applying small drops of different colored samples to the paper, allowing them to dry, then placing the paper in a jar with a small amount of water in the bottom we will see a separation if the dye is composed of several pigments. The small amount of water in the bottom of the jar will travel up the chromatography paper by capillary action and carry the component(s) of the dye with it. Since not all components will be attracted to the water/paper combination to exactly the same extent they will "move up" the paper at different rates, giving a separation. In the case of a mixture of colors, this will give a "rainbow" of different colors. The longer the paper remains in contact with the water the better the separation, so it will be allowed to travel up the paper to within about 1 inch of the top.

The distance traveled by the pigments will be different for different groups in the class because each will allow the water to travel to slightly different heights. There is a quantity, called the R_f value that remains constant regardless of how far the water has traveled and is used to help identify the components in a mixture. The R_f value is defined as

90

$$R_f = \frac{\text{distance spot moved}}{\text{distance solvent moved}}$$

where the "spot" is the food dye component and the solvent is water. Since the spot cannot move any faster than the water, the R_f value must always be less than, or at most equal to, one. You can think of the R_f value as the fractional movement of the spot relative to water. In this experiment you will calculate the R_f value for each spot observed in each sample and then use these R_f values to identify the composition of an unknown.

In our GC experiment, the stationary phase will be a solid support coated with a very viscous (thick) liquid. The mobile phase will be the natural gas from the lab bench. GC is an extremely powerful tool for the separation of complex mixtures and its usefulness is widespread and ever expanding. In fact, people not directly associated with technical fields of study are becoming exposed to this method with increasing regularity. Most urine tests to detect the presence of illegal narcotics are accomplished by GC, as are blood tests to determine alcohol levels of people suspected of being intoxicated. It is presented in courtroom testimony concerning the detection of volatile accelerants, such as gasoline or kerosene, in both civil and criminal cases involving potential arson or the inappropriate substitution of gasoline for kerosene in home heaters.

We are going to carry out the separation using a glass column about 10 inches long that is filled with commercial GC column packing. The column will be attached to the natural gas supply on the lab bench with self-sealing latex tubing. The sample (either a single pure compound or a mixture of compounds) will be injected directly on to the column using a plastic gastight syringe. The carrier gas (the natural gas from the lab bench) will carry the component(s) through the column. Depending on the attractive forces between the component(s) and the column packing, each will travel at a different rate and eventually come off the other end of the column one at a time. This is the basic separation principle behind GC. There is a brief discussion of GC on page 555 of your course textbook Chemistry: The Molecular Science, Third Edition by John W. Moore, Conrad L. Stanitski, and Peter C. Jurs.

Identification in GC is made using a parameter called the retention time, or the amount of time necessary for the component to emerge from the column. It is used much the same way R_f values are used in PC. Let us suppose that we inject a sample of CH_2Cl_2 on to the column and we find that it emerges at 23 seconds. If we now run an unknown material and we find a signal at 23 seconds, we

can suspect that CH_2Cl_2 is in the unknown. In actuality, if the sample is complex and completely unknown, additional testing would be necessary to verify this conclusion, but in this experiment we are intentionally eliminating the complications that can come from more complex mixtures or a completely unknown material. Remember: our objective here is to demonstrate the general principles of GC and not become bogged down with all of the nuances of the method. We shall look at three known materials, determine the retention time for each one, and then work with a mixture of all of the knowns to show that they can be separated. Having completed that, we shall study an "unknown" that may contain any or all of the known materials we investigated. It is important to understand that the retention time will be specific for each column: there is no right or wrong answer regarding the retention time. The right or wrong answer that is derived from GC is the ability to separate a mixture into its respective components, so don't be surprised if your retention times do not match someone else's in the class. What should match is the conclusion you reach about the unknown with regard to the number and identity of component(s). Since it is unlikely that your column will exactly match someone else's in terms of its length or the tightness of the packing, it is just as unlikely that your retention time will be exactly the same.

We now need a way to be able to tell when something is coming off the column, which, in turn, will give us the retention time. Since the unaided eye cannot see the chlorinated hydrocarbon molecules, we need some method of converting them to a readily detectable form. This is done using a Beilstein detector, which is a copper metal coil that is burned in a natural gas flame. When a chlorinated hydrocarbon is burned in the natural gas flame and passed over the copper coil, volatile copper chlorides are generated, which are green in color. This green color can be detected quantitatively by a detector box, which we have built here at Drexel. Since this detector is specific for halogenated hydrocarbons, most other interferences cannot be detected. This reduces the possibility of interferences from compounds other than those of interest.

Just inside the detector box is a metal holder to support the copper coil. When properly inserted in the holder, the copper coil will emit a blue flame if only the carrier gas (natural gas) is emerging from the column. As the halogenated hydrocarbons separately emerge from the column, the flame will turn a characteristic green color. The effluent from the column enters the detector box through a latex tubing connector, is burned in a flame, and passes over the copper coil. The light emitted is focused through the lens, passes through a filter that removes all colors but green, and then passes to

a cadmium sulfide (CdS) detector, which is quantitatively sensitive for the green light generated by the burning halogenated hydrocarbon. As the amount of halogenated hydrocarbon changes, the amount of green light emitted changes and the voltage of the signal from the detector will change. At this point, the detector output is interfaced with a Compaq PC equipped with the Vernier LoggerPro 3 Data Collection System, which will record the signal from the detector box and store the data in a file, and also display it as a chart.

The front panel of the detector box is also fitted with several controls that can be used to optimize the signal from the detector box. These controls are shown in Figure 9.1. On the far left of the box is an offset control that can be used to adjust the zero point. This is used to establish the baseline voltage, or the voltage when there is no green flame present. The numerical value used for the baseline voltage is arbitrary but it is most convenient to set it at zero volts. This can be accomplished by rotating the knob in either direction until the zero point is attained. To the right of this knob are two toggle switches: the one on the left controls the filter which can be flipped on to reduce any excessive "noise" to the baseline, and the one on the right controls the gain, which will enhance the signal if it appears to be too small. These switches are used only if either problem is noticed during your experiment. In addition to these controls, the front of the box also has a hinged lock that can be used to open the detector box to light the flame, insert the copper coil, etc. The top of the box is fitted with a chimney to allow for ventilation and the escape of column effluent combustion products. Also on the front face of the detector box is a connector for a power supply for the CdS detector and plugs to connect the detector output to the LoggerPro System to record the voltage.

FIGURE 9.1 - OUTSIDE FACE OF DETECTOR BOX

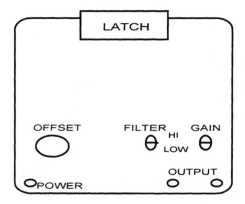

93

In this experiment we are going to determine the retention time of three different halogenated hydrocarbons: methylene chloride (CH_2Cl_2), chloroform ($CHCl_3$), and carbon tetrachloride (CCl_4). From the retention time for each of the three pure compounds it will be possible to determine if an unknown has any or all three of these components in it. The chromatogram for the mixture should show three peaks (one peak for each component) demonstrating that a mixture can be resolved into its respective components. Let us suppose that you investigate three different known materials (which we are going to designate A, B, and C for demonstration purposes) and you observe the following retention times for each component:

COMPONENT	RETENTION TIME (seconds)
A	11
B	18
C	45

If we now analyze an unknown sample and find that it has signals (peaks) at 11 seconds and 45 seconds, we conclude that both components A and C were present in the unknown because the retention times match with those in the table above. To collect the GC data, we are going to interface the detector box to a PC equipped with the Vernier LoggerPro 3 Data Collection System. This experimental setup will automatically record the voltage from the detector box at a predetermined time interval and display the voltage along with a graphical plot of voltage versus time (the chromatogram), but you will not be able to save the graph. You will take the collected data home with you and then reconstruct the chromatograms, which you will need to include with your lab report.

EXPERIMENTAL PROCEDURE

A. PAPER CHROMATOGRAPHY

1. From the front bench obtain a piece of chromatography paper, a ruler and a jar with a lid.

2. Place about 25-30 ml of distilled water into the jar, replace the lid and allow it to sit for about ten minutes to distribute the water vapor throughout the jar. Using too much water tends to cause the paper to become overly saturated because the water travels up the paper too fast and gives poorer separations.

94

3. Using a pencil, draw a line about 2 cm from the bottom of the paper and all the way across. This will be the "starting point" of the experiment where the samples will be applied.

4. Make 5 marks along the pencil line, each about 2 cm apart.

5. In the fume hoods or on the front bench you will find four glass vials with different colored food dyes and a few other vials with samples of concentrated powder drink mixes. Using the toothpick found in each vial, place a very small spot on one of the pencil marks you made. The size of the spot influences the results. Large spots tend to give a lot of tailing and poorer separation than small spots. It is much better to reapply very small spots twice than it is to apply only one big spot. Repeat this for each of the four dyes and the unknown assigned to you so that you have a total of five spots on the paper. Repeat the process so you have two dots of each sample applied to each pencil mark. **TO AVOID CONTAMINATION, DO NOT USE THE SAME TOOTHPICK FOR DIFFERENT SAMPLES.**

6. Fold the paper into a cylinder that will fit inside the jar. Place the paper cylinder inside the jar, replace the lid and allow it to sit undisturbed while the water travels up the paper and separates the dyes into their respective component(s). This typically takes about 30 minutes.

7. While the water is traveling up the paper, you can start Part B of this experiment on GC. Keep your jar nearby so you can periodically check its progress.

8. When the water has traveled to within about an inch from the top, open the jar and remove the paper. Immediately make a mark along the top indicating how far the water has traveled. It might be helpful to put the chromatogram in a drying oven for a few minutes to help it dry so you do not "smudge" the spots.

9. Using your chromatogram, measure each of the following distances (in mm) and record them on your data page. All measurements are made from the initial "starting point" pencil mark you made on the paper.

    -   the distance the solvent moved
    -   the distance each individual colored spot moved for each sample you tested. If any spot is skewed, long, or has a "tail" to it measure the distance to the highest point of progress of the spot

95

B. GAS CHROMATOGRAPHY

1. When you arrive at your work area in the lab, the GC will be already assembled. The glass column will be packed and connected to both the natural gas supply and the detector box with latex tubing. Open the top of the detector box and check to see that there is a copper coil inside. If there is not, obtain one from the front bench.

2. Make sure the power supply and detector box to LoggerPro interface connections are securely made on the front face of the detector box (see Figure 9.1).

3. Open the gas line fully and light the flame over the copper coil inside the detector box. It may take 30 or 40 seconds for the gas to reach the detector box because it has to "percolate" through the column packing. The flame must pass over the copper coil or the detector will be useless. Close the top of the detector box and secure the latch.

4. On the PC desktop you will find an icon labeled **CHEM 102-GC**. Open it by double clicking on the icon. When the application opens, you will see two columns for data: one with a heading of **TIME (s)** and the other with a heading of **POTENTIAL (V)**. When the data are collected, it will be stored in these cells and an immediate graph of the data will appear on the right side of the screen. The graph is only to give you a visual representation of your data during the experimental run and will not be saved. The range of the graph is 0 to 90 seconds (x-axis) for time and -0.2 to 4 volts (y-axis) for potential. This should be more than adequate for your experimental runs. If the potential should exceed 4 volts, don't worry--the data are still being saved but you just cannot see the "upper piece" of the peak. When you construct your own graph from the accumulated data, you can adjust the scale of the axis to show the entire peak. The retention time is the time at which the peak(s) show the maximum voltage.

5. Using the OFFSET control on the front face of the detector box, rotate it in either direction until the voltage displayed on the meter (at the top of the graph, above the y-axis) is near zero volts. CAUTION: A setting of zero is not all the way at the bottom of the screen. The lower limit on the y-axis is set at -0.2 volts. If you turn the OFFSET control too far counterclockwise, you could offset the starting baseline so far down that the peaks will not be seen. When you establish your baseline at near zero volts, there should be an unused portion of the chart seen beneath the baseline.

96

6. At your work area will be a container with five vials in it. There is a separate vial for each of the three known compounds, one for a mixture of the three, and another for the unknown. Also, there will be a syringe to inject the vapors on to the column.

7. Pierce the cap of the sample vial with the syringe needle and withdraw enough vapor **(not liquid)** to give a good detectable signal. This may take some practice. Generally, a good signal can be obtained with only 0.2 to 0.3 ml of CH_2Cl_2. The volumes are not critical and will not affect your data analysis, but you should have an estimate of how much you used. Using too much will cause the peak(s) to become very broad. The narrower the peak, generally the better will be your separation.

8. Pierce the latex tubing with the syringe needle and insert it <u>into the neck</u> of the packed glass tubing column. With one rapid, steady motion inject the vapor on to the column. The quicker the injection, the narrower the peak will be. **At exactly the same time as the injection is begun**, another member of your group should click on the **COLLECT** button at the top of the chart. This will start the data collection. The voltage generated by the detector will be recorded every 0.5 seconds and stored in the spreadsheet. In addition, the graph will be updated every time a new data point is entered. After the peak has emerged, which you will be able to tell by looking at the graph, you can end the run by selecting **STOP** at the top of the screen. If you do not see a peak after about 75 seconds, you probably had a bad injection, and the test must be repeated.

9. Look at the graph to determine if the data are usable. Since this is a single pure compound, you should see only one peak. If there is only one peak and it is easy to see, then this run was a success and you are ready to move on to the next one. Before you inject the next sample, you must save the data. To do this, go up to the **FILE** menu and select **EXPORT AS TEXT**. You will want to save your data to the **DESKTOP**. Give the file a name that you will be able to recognize later when you are doing your report: since the compound studied in this run is CH2CL2, why not use that as the file name?

10. We now have to repeat the above steps on each of the other two known compounds. It is essential to flush the syringe several times with air to make sure you do not have any contamination from the previous sample. You are now ready to move on to the next sample, but the old data are still displayed. Go to the **DATA** menu and select **CLEAR ALL DATA**. This

will remove all old data from the display (but you saved it in its own file) and you are ready to move on to your next sample. Repeat the process described in Steps #7 to #9 for each of the other two pure compounds. Don't forget to save your data after each run, if it appears acceptable. If it does not look acceptable, simply clear the "bad" data and repeat the run, then move on to the next sample after saving the "good" data.

11. Now we need to show that a mixture of the three components can be separated with our GC. Using the same syringe, withdraw a small volume of vapor from the vial labeled "Mixture". Inject the mixture just as you did for the different known components. You should see three peaks: one peak for each component. If you do not, repeat the analysis until a peak appears for each component. Notice the retention time for each peak and observe how they agree (or disagree) with the time you observed for each component separately. If the data appear acceptable, save it as described above, then clear the data from the screen and move on to the last sample.

12. Now that we have seen that a mixture can be separated, we are going to analyze an unknown that may contain any or all of the known materials we tested above. Withdraw a small volume of the vapor of the unknown material and inject it on to the GC column. If the peaks are too wide, you can repeat the analysis using a smaller volume. If the peaks are too small, you can repeat the analysis using a larger volume. Pay particular attention to the region where you noted the peaks in both the known components and the mixture. When you observe an acceptable chromatogram, save the data as described above.

13. When you have collected data for all five samples, go to the **FILE** menu and select **EXIT**. You will be asked if you want to save the changes made to **CHEM 102-GC**. Select **NO** so it will be all set up for the next class. All of the data have already been saved in their own files.

14. When you return to the desktop, you will see your five data files there, identified by the names you assigned. You will need these files to complete your lab report. You can email them to yourself from the PC. The PC is equipped with a wireless Internet card, and you can email the necessary files. Alternatively, you can also transfer them to a USB Flash Drive if you prefer. CAUTION: The computer is already set up for the appropriate wireless connection network. If you try to change to a different one, chances are very good that it will not work properly. DO NOT CHANGE THE WIRELESS NETWORK SETTING.

98

15. After you have transferred your data files, move them to the recycle bin and then delete them from the system. Your instructor will not sign your data sheet until all of these steps have been completed.

TREATMENT OF THE DATA

A. PAPER CHROMATOGRAPHY

1. Calculate and tabulate the R_f value(s) for each spot and look for different samples having the same value(s). This indicates samples having one or more component(s) in common. In calculating the distances the sample and solvent moved, the original pencil line you drew (where the spots were applied) is the starting point.

2. Using the calculated R_f value(s) for the unknown and the known R_f value(s) for the different colored food dyes, determine which dyes are present in the powdered food drink mix you were assigned. Also, comment on any of the "pure" colors that appear to be a mixture of different colors.

B. GAS CHROMATOGRAPHY

1. Open your data files using an application that can be used to graph the data, such as Excel.

2. Construct a chromatogram (a plot of voltage on the y-axis versus time on the x-axis) for each of the five data files. Record the retention time for each peak in the chromatogram of each pure compound. The retention time is when the voltage is at its maximum for any given peak.

3. Examine the retention time for each peak observed in the mixture. Comment on the agreement with the retention time for each single component.

4. Examine the chromatogram for the unknown that you analyzed. Determine the number of components in it by identifying the number of peaks you observed. By comparing the retention times of the peaks in the unknown, determine which of the known compound(s) is/are in the unknown. Since the unknown will have relative composition that is unknown to you, do not be surprised if the sizes of the different peak(s) are significantly different. The size of the peak is a direct measure of the amount of halogenated hydrocarbon in the sample, and there may be just a very slight amount of any one component.

LABORATORY REPORT

Your laboratory report <u>must</u> consist of the following sections, worth the indicated point values:

Procedure (submitted before lab)	5 points
Cover Page	5 points
Introduction	15 points
Data and Calculations	25 points
Observations	10 points
Conclusions/Discussion	25 points
Signed Data Page	15 points

A. The Introduction section must include a brief discussion of the principles of chromatography and your understanding of what the experiment is designed to demonstrate. It is effectively your understanding (but not a direct copy) of the concepts presented in the Background section of this manual.

B. The Data and Calculations section includes all of the computations requested under TREATMENT OF THE DATA, like the tabulation of the respective R_f value(s) in the PC section, along with the construction of the chromatograms and determination of retention times in the GC section.

C. Observations are principally anything that you saw during the experiment such as the number and colors of each spot noticed on the developed PC chromatogram. Indicate whether any of the "pure" food dyes you used appear to be a combination of other colors.

D. Conclusions and Discussion includes your assessment of the components in your unknowns. It must include all reasoning and logic used to arrive at your decision. This section demonstrates your understanding of the concepts and for that reason is worth a large percentage of the grade.

THE PROCEDURE MUST BE SUBMITTED BEFORE YOU DO THE EXPERIMENT. FAILURE TO SUBMIT IT ON TIME WILL GIVE NO POINTS FOR THIS SECTION.

NOTE: Your signed data page must be included with your lab report.

DATA PAGE

PART A - PAPER CHROMATOGRAPHY

Distance solvent (water) moved = _____ mm

NOTE: SPACE IS PROVIDED TO RECORD DATA ON TWO SPOTS FOR EACH COLOR. IF ONLY ONE SPOT IS NOTED, JUST LEAVE THE SECOND LINE BLANK.

	COLOR OF SPOT	**POSITION OF SPOT (mm)**
RED FOOD DYE	_____	_____
	_____	_____
BLUE FOOD DYE	_____	_____
	_____	_____
YELLOW FOOD DYE	_____	_____
	_____	_____
GREEN FOOD DYE	_____	_____
	_____	_____
DRINK MIX	_____	_____
	_____	_____
	_____	_____

INSTRUCTOR'S SIGNATURE_____ DATE_____